Y0-BRS-017

LISTENING TO NATURE — MY CENTURY IN SCIENCE

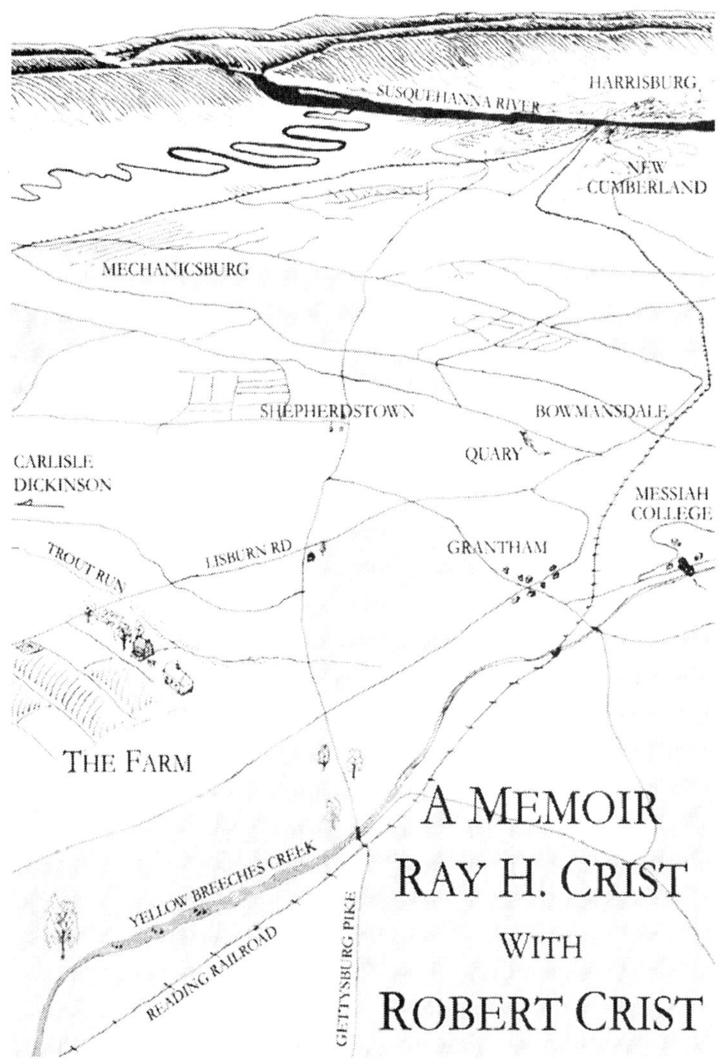

A MEMOIR

RAY H. CRIST

WITH

ROBERT CRIST

LISTENING TO NATURE - MY CENTURY IN SCIENCE

A Memoir

RAY H. CRIST
WITH ROBERT CRIST

Photo Editing by Greg Crist

ISBN 1-59232-080-5 Hardcover
ISBN 1-59232-081-3 Paperback

Printed in the United States of America

Listening to Nature -
My Century in Science

A Memoir

Ray H. Crist

with

Robert Crist

I see the spectacle of morning from the hill-top over against my house, from day-break to sun-rise, with emotions which an angel might share. The long slender bars of cloud float like fishes in the sea of crimson light. From the earth, as a shore, I look out into that silent sea. I seem to partake its rapid transformations: the active enchantment reaches my dust, and I dilate and conspire with the morning wind. How does Nature deify us with a few cheap elements! Give me health and a day, and I will make the pomp of emperors ridiculous. The dawn is my Assyria; the sunset and moon rise my Paphos, and the unimaginable realms of faerie; broad noon shall be my England of the senses and understanding; the night shall be my Germany of mystic philosophy and dreams.

Ralph Waldo Emerson

Acknowledgments

The writing of my memoirs has been a family project. I have shared notes about my life, recollections, and thoughts with Robert, *who—in addition to his own memories and insights—has drawn on archives, remembrances, and ideas from his brothers DeLanson and Henry. As contributing editors, they have given unstintingly of their support and time, offering significant suggestions at every stage of the writing. In turn, my grandson Greg's computer skills have been essential in the photo editing and preparation of the text for publication. My thanks also go to Ross Lenhart, who kindly supplied passages from DeLance Lenhart's unpublished papers. Finally, I wish to thank all those close to me for their ongoing contribution to my day-to-day life.*

R.H.C.

CONTENTS

PROLOGUE

For over ten decades, the world has been calling to me—calling in its natural beauty, tenderness, magic, intricacy, eliciting my responses as growing boy and student, husband and father, researcher and teacher, Manhattan Project scientist and director, industrial chemist and volunteer educator. I recall that H.L. Mencken once said it was the joy of productivity that had fueled his energies as he grew older, yet for him 'nothing could be good forever'. I confess, on the contrary, that the human dreamer in me could gladly envision going on and on 'forever' with unfailing powers and in full partnership with creation. But much as I might fancy it, I can't beat back the stream of time, or—as Henry put it—turn over the great hour-glass of the world. All I can do is count the grains of sand as they flowed and trace them back to their source—a pastoral region called Shepherdstown.

Ray Crist

I'm going out to clean the pasture spring;
I'll only stop to rake the leaves away
(And wait to watch the water clear, I may):
I shan't be gone long. —You come too.

I'm going out to fetch the little calf
That's standing by the mother. It's so young
It totters when she licks it with her tongue.
I shan't be gone long. —You come too.

Robert Frost
"The Pasture"

LIFE ON THE FARM
Shepherdstown, Pennsylvania, 1900-1911

When I came into the world in the year 1900, mankind was on the threshold of vast changes. At the very onset of the new era, however, the foregoing mode of life persisted—especially in the rural countryside. On March 8th of that year I was born—and given the name Ray Henry—in a peaceful old farmhouse near the village of Shepherdstown, Pennsylvania. The two-story brick home, built in the late nineteenth century, lacked indoor plumbing, but it was attractively constructed with a practical layout—a fireplace in every room and a comfortable veranda. It was situated on my family's 80-acre farm with its spring run, barn, shed,

hog-pens, livestock. My father, Henry Dietrich Crist (originally *Christ*), was from a family of German ethnic background who came to Pennsylvania in the 18th century. His father, Samuel Crist—a stoneworker—was a Civil War veteran, who recorded his battle experience near Dismal Swamp in Virginia on the pages of a diary preserved in the archives of the Cumberland County Historical Society. During the war his spouse and their five children were struck down by typhoid. Upon his release from service, Samuel took his second wife, Sarah Cocklin. The Cocklin family (originally *Coquelin*), who were Huguenot refugees, set up the farm, part of which eventually became the property of my father and mother. In his obituary, Samuel Crist was praised as an active, all-round member of the community for whom religious faith was of fundamental importance: "In every department of life he proved his worth and wherever known was recognized as a man among men. He lived a consistent Christian life and for him to die was gain."

My mother, Bertha Crist—also from a farm family of German descent—

was from Trindle Springs. A photograph of Bertha Spera as a girl with a dreamy look in her eye captures her refined features and long, rich, wavy hair. Mother never shared with me any ambitions she might have had to seek horizons beyond rural life in central Pennsylvania. In any case, it was a comely, tireless, young woman, whom Henry Crist was fortunate to take to wife in 1897. Thenceforth, the couple faced the relentless demands of farm life to support themselves and their family, which began to expand with the birth of my brother Guy a year later.

The farm overflowed with living things. We had four horses, ten cows, a hundred chickens, a dozen ducks, and eighty or more hogs. The four fields, running west to Williams Grove Road, were planted with wheat, hay, corn, oats, and potatoes. More than one fourth of our crop went to feed the horses, around which the farm revolved. The horses and mules were our energy source for cultivation and transportation; their manure also fertilized the fields. In this manner, the farm was a self-sustaining entity, in contrast to agriculture in the era of mechanization and the internal-combustion engine which came to dominate the nation's life after the First World War.

As I observed the replacement of the horse by the tractor, and witnessed the advent of nuclear power to supplement dwindling supplies of fossil fuels, I realized that my first decade coincided with an older way of life that had persisted for centuries, but was all too swiftly passing away through the course of the twentieth century. The self-energizing farm, drawing on the power of sunlight, combined with that of man and animals, is a mode of living which continues to this day to hold a powerful appeal for me. Thus, I've never ceased to feel deep nostalgia for the old ways before what I call 'the Passing of the Horse'.

There was not a moment in that childhood world which was not filled with activity—a host of farm tasks, a family effort, and all sorts of contacts with animals in the surrounding environment. Looking back from the decades of my maturity to my earliest years, I see that the unceasing chores of the farm ingrained a work habit in me—the conviction that there are always countless things to be done, and one must never fail to turn to the pressing activity at hand. From the time of my very first chores as a child, I never found working unpleasant, but—on the contrary—considered it an unfailing pleasure. An innate affinity for the strenuous life was probably reinforced by several Horatio Alger books, a number of MacGuffy readers and other works of the kind, which I eagerly read in childhood. Many of these volumes remained on our library shelves up to the 1950's. Nevertheless, despite the notion of the 'work ethic', I never thought of a job as an obligation. Instead, I found it rewarding and invigorating in itself. At the turn of the 21st century, whenever I was asked what 'kept me working' as a centenarian in the laboratory, I always replied, "Why, I don't call that 'work'! I just keep on enjoying getting my fingers into things and exploring the nature of life. That's all I'm doing."

On our farm, the source of the spring was not far from our house, and the spring run was accessible in our cellar. There was also a small spring house built over the run a few steps from the porch. This was used to refrigerate our

milk products and other produce. The pristine and delightfully cold water running through the spring house contained fish and snakes. Especially fascinating were superb rainbow trout, up to twenty inches. These fish grew accustomed to us boys lifting them out of the water, almost like pets, onto the plank. Returning them to the stream, we fed them minnows and sparrows, which they eagerly consumed.

Through play I related to the creatures of the countryside. Guy and I built small dams across the run to pursue the minnows, which were very lively and hard to catch. Muskrats inhabited numerous burrows along the run near the cress patches. We went after them with traps, ending up over the course of a winter with thirty pelts, which we sold for fifteen cents a piece to glove makers. Skunks liked to scramble around the Cocklin Cemetery bordering our fields, boring into the church cellar and digging up bones from graves. We chased them down, accumulating yearly around eight pelts worth twenty cents each. Snakes were a matter of concern. I recall glimpsing a copperhead sliding out of the spring house. Dashing to the run, I caught him by the tail, slammed him to the ground and stamped on his head. Once while loading hay, I pitched up a rattler. Leaping to the ground, I grabbed a stick and dispatched him.

Horses and mules were at the very center of our lives. I cared for them, shared tasks with them and observed their distinct behavior. Kate and Ann, our white mules, worked day-in, day-out, cultivating and hauling. While wayward Ann kept drifting away from the row, dependable Kate ploughed a true line down the field. Through the course of a day I petted her with a special sense of gratitude. After many years, Ann was sold and a cloud descended over Kate's life.

An incident involving a horse could have cut my life short virtually at the start. I was two years old. As I learned later, the accident occurred on an ordinary day during a leisurely drive in our wagon. The family had picked up an uncle and aunt in Mechanicsburg. The wagon was drawn by a spry pony and I was sitting in the back seat. Suddenly, a possum darted across the road ahead, the horse reared and I was thrown between the wheel and chassis onto the ground. Rushing to my aid—the story goes—my parents found with immense relief that I appeared fit as a fiddle. I was terribly frightened, but indeed there were apparently no serious injuries—only a few minor scratches and bruises. If I were of a fanciful turn of mind, perhaps I would later have thought of my survival not as sheer luck, but as a heavenly sign. Anyhow, after a brief precautionary confinement to bed, I was good as new! It was a different case for a neighbor years later when a runaway bull came raging across our meadow. My brother and I took a swift evasive course and my father hoisted himself to a tree limb. A sluggish neighbor, however, was suddenly set upon by the rampaging animal and paid with his life.

From the age of eight, I busied myself in daily farm work—bringing in hay, slaughtering hogs, preparing cuts of meat, milking cows, cleaning up the stable, spreading manure, and so forth. I grew used to working barefoot. I delighted in the feel of the earth underfoot and the grain of an axe or pitchfork handle in my hands. I also enjoyed risky boyhood skills like negotiating the high barn rafters like a tight-rope walker. As I engaged in daily jobs, I came to admire my father's drive and sense of organization. He went into hog-raising shrewdly and systematically. The accompanying picture shows my father proudly contemplating one of his prize animals. He concocted a special diet for our four score pigs, feeding them on mash, a by-product of a local distillery, combined with skimmed milk produced by our cows. This made savory, nourishing fare for our porkers. The mash was stored in a large barrel near the pens, and the feed was then distributed from a barrel on wheels along the length of the troughs. The

pampered animals grew at a prodigious rate and produced very fine ham and pork. During the winter, twice a week we butchered four hogs. The hams were pickled, then cured with hickory smoke for two weeks and finally hung in the house attic for sale the following summer. The remaining cuts of meat were sold at Harrisburg market. Every Tuesday and Thursday night, my parents would pack the wagon and drive four hours to market, arriving at the crack of dawn. There they served a variety of customers, including Hungarian steel workers from Steelton. From time to time, when my father was busy elsewhere, I would accompany mother on the midnight trip to market. Aiding her in this effort gave me a sense that I was an able 'young man' in the family, pulling my weight in the mutual enterprise.

My first school of science was life on the farm and in the rural countryside. I observed with fascination the intricate characteristics of the natural world, the features and processes of animal life, the interaction of animals and nature, of human beings with the environment. My curiosity was aroused as to the workings of nature and the question of why things are as they are. What was it, for example, in the lay of the land that caused the ground on one side of our run to be of clay, while the other side was limestone soil? In human behavior, what led some people to face challenges patiently, productively, while others were angry, aggressive, and self-defeating? What made a person creative in one aspect of his life and inept, if not destructive, in another? What was behind the magic of one's contact with the world—that delightful affinity with plants and animals, that sense of awe and wonder before the magnitude and complexity of creation?

Our hired man, Melvin Sauder, was a study in human behavior. He was with us many years. Melvin was a dependable worker all right, but he was an equally devoted tippler. Every Saturday evening he'd mosey over to the Mechanicsburg bar and drink himself into a stupor. My brother and I were assigned to fetching him back to his room in the shed. Uncomplainingly, we half-walked, half-dragged him home, where he spent Sunday morning recovering in the sack. On Monday morning, he was back on the job—never, as I recall, acknowledging our role in his Saturday peregrinations. Nor did he ever evidence development in any facet of his life—he just plodded along on the job and then drank away on the weekends.

While my soft-spoken mother was reserved, thoughtful and centered on the home and farm-work, my enterprising, restless and sometimes irritable father was the epitome of action on multiple fronts. Around 1910, he made a great find, purchasing a ten horse-power gasoline engine, the only one in two townships. For my active-minded old man, this versatile power-source was a godsend. With it we

threshed our wheat and performed the same service for neighbors throughout the harvest season. Father also adapted the machine to crush stone in the quarry for use in paving. He worked on construction of the Gettysburg Pike and he even applied the machine to wood-cutting. In another capacity, he became a skilled auctioneer, organizing six-week sales each spring. Always energetic, he would pace our living room as he enthusiastically honed his auctioneer's spiel. Certain items from sales would remain in the family's possession, and he was especially fond of clocks (as I myself am, to this day). One of these was a nineteen-century wooden works clock made by Eli Terry, as yet ticking away in the home of my son, Lance. Two other pendulum clocks (with brass works) are in my living room and porch study. There was an occasion when one of the items for auction—a hotel!—didn't sell, and father took charge of it for a time, without success. Furthermore, an avid Republican, dad was dynamic and versatile in local political life. Over the years, he was involved in election campaigns, the school committee, and supervision of road-maintenance.

In matters of religion, my mother and father were on opposite sides of the fence. Grandmother Sarah Messinger Spera lived with us. She and mother attended church services from time to time in Mechanicsburg, and the good pastor paid them visits four or five times a year. Grand-dad Sammy Crist had been deeply pious. His Civil War diary shows that the violence of battle weighed upon his conscience, and it appears that religious faith provided spiritual consolation. He stated, for example, that in one skirmish his regiment came under such heavy fire that it appeared providential not a single soldier was killed and the wounds were slight. "No doubt almighty God remembered well," he mused, "that we did not come voluntarily to take the life that we cannot give, but being drafted, he did have compassion on us." As a man of faith, he was concerned that his son, Henry, would also cultivate spiritual awareness. The boy's inclination, however, was not in that direction—as shown in dad's refusal to share in mother's belief.

Father's younger sister, my Aunt Ida, was the teacher in the one-room schoolhouse, located at Center Square, a mile and a half from our home. Aunt Ida was a tall, vigorous, good-hearted young woman whose very presence was a blessing. As I remember her alert, strong, cheerful face, I believe that she would have been a fitting subject for a painting by Norman Rockwell. An

accompanying photo shows the Center Square School—Aunt Ida and her pupils. I am the one holding the plaque, and Guy is the second student to my left. When Guy began school at the age of six, Aunt Ida said, "Let Ray come along; he'll be no trouble," and as a result I was granted a running start at life—entering college, then, at the age of sixteen. I recall nothing particularly unusual happening during those opening school years, though Aunt Ida discovered that at first, as I sat on an opposite seat, I was managing to read upside-down the book held by my brother.

Guy and I were always together and our classmates gave us the rhyming nick-names 'Raysor' and 'Geyser'. These monikers were a superb defeat of my father's intentions in naming us as he did. He had been nick-named 'Henny', which was particularly galling to a fellow who deemed himself a 'rooster'. Thus, he had given us the short, snappy names Ray and Guy, he said, to preclude the assignment of silly nick-names! Under Aunt Ida's kind tutelage, those years were a happy and effective introduction to learning. Nevertheless, there was a big change coming, for without a hint to us, father was about to effect a development in our schooling.

When you start on your journey to Ithaca,
then pray that the road is long,
full of adventure, full of knowledge.
Do not fear the Lestrygonians
and the Cyclopes and the angry Poseidon.
You will never meet such as these on your path,
if your thoughts remain lofty, if a fine
emotion touches your body and your spirit.
You will never meet the Lestrygonians,
the Cyclopes and the fierce Poseidon,
if you do not carry them within your soul,
if your soul does not raise them up before you. . .

Constantine Cavafy
from "Ithaca"
(Translated by Rae Dalven)

MESSIAH BIBLE SCHOOL AND MISSIONARY TRAINING HOME
Grantham, Pennsylvania, 1911-1916

There was a major change coming for Guy and me one Monday morning in February when I was eleven years old. Without informing us, father had been contemplating an upgrade from the demands of Aunt Ida's old-fashioned one-room school. With his usual look of determination, father announced to his sons out of the clear blue sky, "Come, boys, I'm going to take you where, for a change, you'll get plenty of homework!" With no further explanation, he drove us to Grantham where he enrolled us at Messiah Bible School and Missionary Training Home, which later grew into Messiah College, a liberal arts college which has maintained a strong religious tradition. As a lad of eleven, I hardly could have imagined that at Messiah I would daily be devoting the closing decades of the century to the pursuit of environmental research with test-tubes, beakers, pH meters, and a spectrometer. The fact was that, had I not been able to complete my high school education at Messiah, I might not have been able to complete it at all, since the high school at Mechanicsburg was too great a distance to facilitate daily attendance by Guy and me.

At that time a single large building at Messiah provided space for classes, administration, chapel services, and dormitory rooms. The schooling was effective, and we attended chapel services daily. During this period my heart was strongly drawn to spiritual concerns. I caught the fervor of chapel sessions and regularly attended Sunday morning services in Shepherdstown church, as well as youth programs and vespers. I must admit, though, that as a small boy, along with Guy, I had not been immune years before to inappropriate behavior on the church premises. One frosty Winter Sunday morning we were tagging along with a group of mischievous whippersnappers who snuck into the entrance hall of the church. From the sanctuary could be heard the sounds of the congregation singing hymns. Little did they know that an unruly band of Tom Sawyers was about to play a deliciously nasty trick on them. In a cloak-room off the hall were hundreds of mud-caked galoshes which the churchgoers had scrupulously removed before entering the church proper. In a fit of glee, the naughty boys invaded the cloak-room, gathered up all the overshoes, and—with no further ado—tossed them into the creek! Guy and I (who looked on without participating) fled the scene filled with mixed feelings of amusement and guilt.

As a maturing older lad at Messiah School, I found adolescence to be a period of blossoming feelings and heartfelt probing. Sunday afternoons I would climb to the high limbs of a tall oak tree by our house, and there—

suspended between earth and heaven—I pondered the goings on of animal life beneath the leaves and the working of the divine throughout the universe. Reading scripture avidly, I wished to share my insights and inspirations. This led to my teaching a youth Bible study class at church and—at the age of sixteen—being assigned a place on the deacons' bench next to the pulpit. Many years later, I found

a wooden bench of this type, a 'settee', that is now in my study—used, not as a place to sit, but as a handy surface for 'filing' stacks of data from my laboratory research.

Though my belief was fervent, I saw during these years that the ministry did not appear to be my calling. This was a disappointment to the church community, and word got around that my father had influenced my decision. (This rumor was baseless, of course, for though—to be sure—I possessed some of my father's traits, I was never hesitant to oppose him outrightly in regard to certain attitudes and values.) Hearing this unsupportable but irritating rumor, father was furious. He hustled me to the car and drove at top-speed to the parsonage, where he confronted the mild-mannered pastor at the front door. Pushing me forward, he sputtered, "Tell them, Ray—tell them, son!—that I've got *nothing—nothing what-so-ever!*— to do with your religious notions!"

Though I did not choose the ministry, my experience at Messiah significantly influenced my attitudes. I never believed in mere words but felt that a prayerful approach to actions was the goal, and that I should always strive to do right. A bible in my library—given to me by an aunt and uncle on March 8, 1912—is marked by my penciled notations. In Psalms, I see I wrote in the margin, "Songs of Pilgrimage," "The light of life, the knowledge of God," and "The inspiration of devotion, the true wealth." In Micah 6, I marked the famous verse, telling myself "Learn [by heart]": "He hath shewed thee, O man, what is good; and what doth the Lord require of thee, but to do justly, and to love mercy, and walk humbly with thy God?" I can say that not only the religious feeling but also the kindness and harmony of relationships at Messiah are reflected in my lifelong conviction that contention should be avoided in personal and professional relations. Instead, give-and-take makes for both inspiring and creative relationships. In turn, I would be a churchgoer up to the time in my life (after I passed 100) when my movement outside the house became limited.

As graduation from Messiah School approached, our parents' hopes for our progress, combined with Aunt Ida's concern with learning, were pointing my brother and me toward college. Guy already had his heart set on becoming a physician; a house-call from a doctor during a minor illness seems to have oriented him toward pre-medical work. I was as yet uncertain of my life's goal. Nonetheless, my unforgettable boyhood years on the farm, packed with experience, curiosity, and observation, prepared me for entrance into academia.

Men, my brothers, men the workers,
ever reaping something new:
That which they have done but earnest
of the things that they shall do…

Alfred Tennyson
from "Locksley Hall"

DICKINSON COLLEGE AND WILLIAMSPORT-DICKINSON SEMINARY
Carlisle & Williamsport, Pennsylvania, 1916-1921

In 1916, Guy and I enrolled at Dickinson College. During our freshman year, after the daily feeding of the animals, I would walk with my brother to take the Dillsburg trolley to Mechanicsburg, where we took the train to Carlisle. In our sophomore year, we commuted to and from school in a Model A Ford which my father purchased for that purpose. I remember that even when Lisburn Road was unplowed, and we had to drive through deep snow, the Model A proved to be a tough, dependable mode of transportation. After two years, Guy completed pre-med work and went on to Jefferson Medical College in Philadelphia. During my two final years at Dickinson, I had a room on campus. On vacations, holidays, and weekends, I continued to work on the farm, though I spent a portion of one summer smashing stone with a sledge hammer at the Bowmansdale quarry, and another summer I was an itinerant salesman in Indiana farm country, peddling books on veterinary medicine. I can't say that line of work offered anything of interest. In fact, I remember that on one farm I asked to 'earn my supper' by lending a hand all afternoon in the fields. What a relief it was to be active again and be able to replace my peddler's pitch with pitching hay.

At college, hours spent in the classroom and library were supremely enriching and delightful. This was indeed my element! I was intensely drawn to the natural sciences, particularly to chemistry, but I was also exhilarated by history, Latin, and literature. To an inexperienced youth of limited background, the epic of historic events, the exploits of great men, and the achievements of human thought were deeply inspiring—though of course sometimes daunting. Each moment of study was a fresh revelation. I was enamored of the features of language—the skills demanded in writing, the richness of the English tongue, the elegant structure of Ciceronian Latin. In turn, I developed a life-long love of literature—for example, the writings of Shakespeare, Tennyson, Burns, and Wordsworth.

In the course of my freshman year, the president of the college—Dr. Morgan—happened to speak to me as I was crossing the quadrangle. "Young man," he said kindly, "you should stand up straight as you walk!" I realized that perhaps my posture had been affected by bending over the plow, and I responded with gratitude to his advice. That exchange with the president may have been the beginning of his awareness of my record at the college. As a result, in the summer of my sophomore year, I received a letter from him suggesting that I go to Plattsburgh in upstate New York for Army training preparatory to

becoming a drill-sergeant in the military training program on campus. The efforts and duties of boot-camp were no strain for a young fellow disciplined by farm life. Through the course of the summer, I even gained weight on mess-hall chow, bringing me up to one hundred and fifty pounds. Soon thereafter, I dropped back to one hundred forty-five, which I maintained throughout my life.

During the following academic year, you find me drilling a squad of twenty students, doing athletic exercises in the morning and marching in rank on the football field in the afternoon. Working barefoot on the farm so many years, I found that wearing thick, tight army boots took a heavy toll on my feet. Much worse, however, was my duty of demonstrating to my trainees how an enemy soldier was done in with a brutal thrust of the bayonet, as taught by our French instructor at training camp. I will never forget my feeling of horror in contemplating such an act.

In the fall of 1919, an unexpected challenge arose. I was asked to participate in an intercollegiate cross-country race. My classmates had evidently gotten wind of the fact that I habitually preferred to run—rather than walk—to where I was going, be it from church to home, or home to trolley-stop. Though the thought of participating in athletic games never crossed my mind, I was willing enough to run with the Dickinson team. Without coaching, that was the only event I ever entered, and—much to my surprise— I placed second in competition with experienced, trained runners. I might add that our coach praised me for doing a six-minute mile. When I look at today's athletic shoes, I realize that I was probably running in ordinary street shoes, but it seems my work-toughened feet enabled me to take that in stride!

In my senior year, my experience rose to a peak, for that was the time that the greatest joy of my being—Dorothy—appeared. Dorothy Pauline Lenhart was from New Cumberland. She had taken a year's leave from her studies at Irving Female College in Mechanicsburg in order to contribute to her family's support. She was teaching at a school in Shepherdstown, and from time to time she would hitch a ride with my father to her school. However, I first set eyes on Dorothy in church. After services, a group of us young fellows would traipse along behind the bevy of gals as they strolled through the countryside. Before long, Dorothy and I were walking together, immediately becoming very close. This was my first—and never to be equaled—experience of deep sharing in heart and soul. From moment to moment our rapport flowered though the years. I do not have words to describe the feelings I shared with this gentle, radiant girl whose heart was so filled with love of life and people.

DeLanson Lenhart (or DeLance, as he liked to be called) and his wife Clara had four children—the older daughters, Miriam and Dorothy, son DeLanson (nicknamed Mark, and later Nick), and the youngest girl, Vira. Dorothy's dad had been in the roofing business, but in mid-life he was stricken with crippling arthritis, confining him to a wheelchair. Highly sociable and witty, he was a superb storyteller—a popular personality in the area. His hobby was building model frigates, one of which is still around after all these years. A leader in town politics, he was appointed Justice-of-the Peace, and we affectionately referred to him as Squire Lenhart. At the end of his life, as I will discuss later in detail, he achieved recognition as a story-teller in the tradition of Mark Twain, Sherwood Anderson, and Sinclair Lewis.

My wonderful Dorothy was dubbed 'Dottie' by her family—a humorous nick-name which was used by many friends. I, however, loved the name Dorothy and was delighted to learn that it means 'the gift of God'. To visit Dorothy at her home, I would run through the fields to the trolley station, and then take the train for the eight miles to New Cumberland. She filled my life with inspiration and blessedness. Our mutual feelings became the core of our existence. How vividly I recall a wonderful evening in the summer of 1920. I was sitting on the porch dreaming of her. My mind was overflowing with tender thoughts, and my heart was brimming with love. In an overpowering impulse, it came to me: this very evening—as soon as possible!—I would put into words the proposal which had been taking shape in our hearts. I hurried to her home and with a lump in my throat asked for her hand in marriage. Oh how moving it was to see the happiness lighting her face and hear her sweet words of acceptance. I returned home in ecstasy. The next day in the field I pulled weeds all morning, swept away with the feeling that providence had granted us the blessing of a lifetime. How those weeds flew! Dorothy was welcomed with open arms by my family, as they shared in our joy.

Graduation from Dickinson came in June, 1920. At this juncture in my life, I was still uncertain of my profession. Before college, as I mentioned, I had briefly contemplated the pastor's life. I realized, however, that I had not experienced an authentic calling to a pastoral mission. Time and time again, meditating high up in the oak tree, I was crushed by receiving no remarkable transcendent experience. It was true, too, that the day-to-day activities of a man of the cloth held little appeal. Rather, I felt increasing excitement toward the challenging intricacies of the natural world.

As summer approached and Dorothy anticipated returning to Irving for her senior year, I wondered what would be my present course. My quandary was resolved by yet another letter from President Morgan, this time enjoining me to apply for a science teaching post that was open at Williamsport-Dickinson Seminary (later Lycoming College). This was a Methodist-sponsored residential co-educational academy north of Harrisburg. My application accepted I entered whole-heartedly into teaching and directing related lab work in the areas of chemistry, physics, and biology. My responsibilities included presiding over a dining hall table and supervising a dorm wing. It was an eye-opening, rewarding year that led me further into the fields of education and chemistry. My sight, however, was now fixed on a career in higher education. The guileless farm boy was headed for the big city!

RAY H. CRIST

> *. . . And this prayer I make,*
> *Knowing that Nature never did betray*
> *The heart that loved her; 'tis her privilege*
> *Through all the years of this our life, to lead*
> *From joy to joy. . . .*
>
> William Wordsworth
> from "Tintern Abbey"

COLUMBIA UNIVERSITY
New York, New York, 1921-1928

In the summer of 1921, I enrolled for graduate studies in the Department of Chemistry at Columbia University. As it turned out, my sweetheart was by my side in New York to share my joys and prospects as my new venture began. To compensate for a gap in my undergraduate studies, I was taking an analytical chemistry course, and Dorothy had a scholarship for summer session at the Teacher's College division of Columbia University. Together we explored Manhattan and went on excursions into the suburbs, including a picnic at Tarrytown, which Dorothy found enchanting as the locale of Washington Irving's tales. Tarrytown would prove to be the starting point of one of the circles that constituted a pattern in my life, since at that site many decades later I would undertake the directorship of the Union Carbide Research Institute.

Dorothy returned to her final year at Irving in the fall of 1921, at which time she anticipated it would take five years before we could be married, in order that she could complete her degree and earn certification through working as a teacher. She was very keen about this goal because she valued a teaching career (which she did pursue up to 1938). We would be seeing one another when I could get away from New York on vacations, or she could come over for a

visit.

So here I was that fall in the magical world of the Columbia Chemistry Department, but without any clue as to how I would survive, let alone flourish or work any magic of my own. Setting out on my professional career, I was greatly inspired but found myself in a highly precarious position. Completely on my own, I was as yet virtually unknown to the Chemistry faculty. Having arrived with a mere two hundred dollars, I had only enough money to pay one semester's tuition. Without a scholarship or other means of support, I was completely uncertain both where the next meal was coming from and where fate would take me in academia. I wondered whether I would be waiting tables to eke out support or whether some paying assignment might be open in the department.

Unsure that anything might be available, I checked with the professor in charge of undergraduate laboratory sessions. He told me that no lab assistant openings were available. However, someone was needed to set up and perform demonstrations for undergraduate lecture courses. Indeed, with great relief and enthusiasm, I began this work at once, and it suited me in every respect, for I had always been excited by hands-on involvement in experiments. I approached a problem energetically with deep curiosity, eager to let the phenomena speak for themselves and fascinated by working out procedures which would best illuminate the processes. In the Physical Chemistry course, I not only set up a series of experiments in the thermostatic process but suggested improvements in each phase of the demonstrations. Professor Jacob J. Beaver commended my performance to Professor J. Livingston Rutgers Morgan, who became my mentor for research in Photochemistry. His specific line of investigation, however, did not work out for me, so after a year I broke fresh ground on my own—the result, three papers appearing in the *Journal of the American Chemical Society*.

In the fall of 1924, as I was pressing forward on my research for the doctorate, I was supported in my strenuous efforts by letters from Dorothy and the thought that we would be married in the coming June. Our mutual joy is reflected in Dorothy's diary of 1925. It is only now, as I

write my memoirs, that I summon the strength to read her words, so that I can suppress the pain of losing her and calmly take myself back to those youthful days of love with no dark clouds on the horizon. Dorothy repeatedly tells her 'Little Book' how delightful it is to receive 'Specials'—regular letters from her sweetheart, and she keeps within the diary's pages a little valentine heart I sent her, inscribed in white ink, "Miss Lenhart," along with a small arcade photo of me. On March 8th of the year, she celebrates, "My Ray's twenty-fifth birthday!" as she anticipates our being together in New York— "Dear Summer and Ray and Columbia." My beloved Dorothy's words are especially touching to me as I hear her speak of fulfillment through our love and the spiritual values of our marriage. In January, she writes tenderly, "I have always been happy but with Ray I will be complete"; and in June—as the wedding day approaches—she speaks so beautifully of the promise of our future: "Dear Ray, our plans are so happy. Our ideals are high and true & we, Ray, can live them."

Thus, on June 30, 1925, we were married "as the

clock struck ten" (Dorothy symbolically notes in her diary). It was a double wedding at the home of an aunt in York: Dorothy and I; her sister Miriam and Douglas Beidel, who were always to remain very close to us. As we left to begin our life together in Manhattan, my heart was ringing with Burns's lines, "As fair art thou, my bonnie lass, / So deep in love am I: / And I will love thee still, my dear, / Till a' the seas gang dry. . .". Thus, with high hearts, my matchless 'bonnie' wife and I were off at last to our first home, an apartment on 125th Street! While I pursued my teaching and research in chemistry, receiving my Ph.D. in 1926, Dorothy progressed toward a Master's Degree in Literature at Columbia University. She was truly absorbed in her studies, and no wonder, for she was taking courses under such noted and eloquent scholars as Carl Van Doren. Columbia University was opening wide vistas for us both, and in 1928 we were also able to explore the world of Europe, which offered its own startling achievements in science and the arts. I had succeeded in competition for a research fellowship abroad. So, we were about to set out on our pilgrimage to the cultural shrines of Europe, as well as on my academic odyssey to the Mecca of contemporary science, Berlin.

We shall not cease from exploration
And the end of all our exploring
Will be to arrive where we started
And know the place for the first time.

. . . . . .

At the source of the longest river
The voice of the hidden waterfall
And the children in the apple tree.

. . . . . .

Where the tongues of flame are in-folded
Into the crowned knot of fire
And the fire and the rose are one.

T.S. Eliot
from "Little Gidding"
Four Quartets

THE EUROPEAN PILGRIMAGE AND THE BODENSTEIN LAB
Berlin, 1928-1929

Thus, our European experience of 1928-1929 combined, if you like, the rose of the arts and history with the fire of the chemistry laboratory. Dorothy's diary of Spring, 1928, helps refresh my memory of how busy those times were for us as our August embarkation for Europe approached. She writes of registering with a teacher's agency, job-hunting, keeping house in our Grantwood, New Jersey, apartment, and meeting me from time to time in the city. She confirms my recollection that I frequently had to spend extended time in the lab, for she notes that there are evenings she feels lonely and longs for me to be home.

It was, then, with a great sense of relief and expectation that we looked forward to nine months away from the regimented schedule, when there would be time both for my uninterrupted research and our extensive touring together. That year constituted, in effect, a sabbatical (and the only one I ever had).

The William Bayard Cutting Traveling Fellowship was a university award for an academic year of research under a leading scientist in Europe. I chose to go to Berlin. Dorothy and I embarked from Pier 4, Hoboken, on August 22, 1928, aboard the *S.S. George Washington* (Stateroom 635), United States Lines. As she notes in her travel journal, briefly aboard the ocean liner to see us off were sister Miriam, our good friend Julie Britton, my close colleague, J.J. Beaver, and Dorothy's cousin, always lively Al Mathias. After a smooth eight-day crossing we docked at the historic English

harbor of Plymouth.

With Smeaton Lighthouse opposite Drake's island and the sheltered bay surrounded by fortressed isles, Plymouth is a splendid gateway to the landscape and history of Europe. Handing over our landing permits, we checked into a charming old hotel and immediately set out to walk the moors overlooking the sound. At the top of the hill we

strolled through 'The Hoe', beautiful gardens from which we enjoyed the panorama of the seascape. Mists added their ethereal touch to the scene as we took in the historic atmosphere. It was here in Plymouth that Sir Francis Drake was playing bowls when the Spanish Armada came into sight. Here, too, Sir John Hawkins and Sir Walter Raleigh figured in the dramatic developments of the time. Of interest to us also was an impressive Memorial Monument of the World War. Everywhere we traveled in Europe war monuments and battlefield sites would remind us that the tragedy of the war was still painfully alive in memory.

The next day we arrived at the picturesque ruins of Okehampton Castle. Its setting on the hill offered a breathtaking view, and 'Lady Howard's walk' extended about two miles through holly tree groves and old oaks. Dorothy commemorated the delights of the day by picking four myrtle leaves to paste in her journal. In turn, we viewed the singularly beautiful harbor in Clovelly, and then moved on to Exeter, where the magnificent cathedral standing amidst old houses was deeply evocative of life in past ages. The cathedral's tall stained glass windows truly inspired a sense of reverence and divine beauty. On the worldly side, Mol's Coffee House, opposite the cathedral, welcomed the eager traveler with the oak-paneled club room that had been a favorite haunt of Raleigh, Drake, and Sir Humphrey Gilbert.

At the town of Ottery St. Mary the following day, we had our first opportunity to visit a literary shrine, for this was the birthplace of Samuel Taylor Coleridge, and the churchyard contained his descendant's graves. Our literary tour continued with a visit to the Fleet Street locale in London, the neighborhood of Samuel Johnson's professional activities. A major high point in our tour of England was our pilgrimage to Stratford-on-Avon, where it was touching to stand on the very ground on which Britain's gift to the world—William Shakespeare—was born and died. In Stratford, by the way, we came upon a couple, who also turned out to be American tourists. Their family, we learned, owned a department store in Harrisburg. Why, we were also from the area, we told them. Their name was Bowman, and their ancestors had founded the town of Bowmansdale. Why that's near Shepherdstown, we said—our stomping grounds. Imagine that—we Pennsylvanians meeting at Shakespeare's shrine, and they with the picturesque name of *Bowman*, so reminiscent of England's days of old.

In the Lake District, Dorothy and I experienced a special blend of the breathtaking landscape and literary memory, since we visited Nether Stowey, where Wordsworth and Coleridge worked together so productively on the innovative collection *Lyrical Ballads*. We stood together meditatively before the Memorial Tablet to

Wordsworth in Grasmere Church. Later on the moors, I recited a passage from *Tintern Abbey*, recalling that there was a special touch in the poem for us, seeing that Wordsworth ended the work addressing his sister, Dorothy:

> *. . . My dear, dear Sister! . . . this prayer I make*
> *Knowing that nature never did betray*
> *The heart that loved her; 'tis her privilege*
> *Through all the years of this our life, to lead*
> *From joy to joy: for she can so inform*
> *The mind that is within us, so impress*
> *With quietness and beauty, and so feed*
> *With lofty thoughts, that neither evil tongues,*
> *Rash judgments, nor the sneers of selfish men,*
> *Nor greetings where no kindness is, nor all*
> *The dreary intercourse of daily life,*
> *Shall e'er prevail against us, or disturb*
> *Our cheerful faith, that all which we behold*
> *Is full of blessings. . .*

On September 10th — 15th we rounded out our tour

of England by walking around the magnificent ruins of

Kenilworth Castle in Warwickshire and then visiting Edinburgh, whose strongest association for Dorothy was Sir Walter Scott, while mine, of course, was Robert Burns.

In England, Dorothy and I had combined bicycling and train transportation; we also brought our bikes along on the boat-train crossing the channel. Looking for an institute for my project, we went to Dahlem, a suburb southwest of Berlin where two of the famous Kaiser Wilhelm Institutes were located, one for chemistry and one for physical chemistry. Managing no contact there, I went to Berlin and was accepted to pursue research under Professor Max Bodenstein. Before discussing my work there, I will turn to the wonderful odyssey which on vacation took us through Germany, over to Vienna, and down to Italy. For Dorothy, of course, it was the Germany of Schiller and Goethe, Strauss and Wagner that was, above all, of interest. So while we froze in our hotel room, Dorothy's heart was especially warmed by the operas and concerts we attended in Berlin. We were entertained by *Der Rosenkavalier* at the Oper unter den Linden; we were impressed by *Boris Gudunov*, and were moved by *Die Meistersinger*, which was my favorite operatic work. As a violinist, Dorothy was profoundly affected by the concert performance of Fritz Kreisler. She found his choice of selections 'soothing' and his 'manner' of playing 'perfect'.

While my weekdays were occupied at the laboratory, Dorothy frequented the museums where I would sometimes join her in the afternoon. Weekends and holidays at the University gave us the opportunity to go on excursions outside Berlin.

In early January, we took our first trip beyond Germany. Staying briefly in Paris, we walked over battlefields around Verdun. On the road to Malancourt we found grim mementoes of The Great War—a rusty revolver and bayonet. At Verdun itself we were particularly affected by terrible visages of violence: Fort Vaux, underground passages, and rusty shells in the fields. There were ten military burial vaults and several monuments to the unknown who had fallen in battle. On the way back to Berlin, we had a very exciting and pleasant trip to Trier and the Moselle Valley. I was truly carried away examining what Dorothy called "unexcelled stony history": churches, basilica, amphitheaters, Roman and Kaiser baths, and a Roman bridge still in use.

Our climactic experience of European culture came in our tour in March and April of Dresden, Freiburg, Prague, Vienna, Trieste, Venice, Florence, and Rome. As we set out on March 25th, Dorothy whispered softly to me that I should consider the much-deserved upcoming holiday my 'birthday present' and she noted on the first page of her journal, "Geburtstag, Heinrichs, Mar. 8, '29." In Dresden we attended a performance of *Parsifal*, and the overwhelming architectural beauty of the city was complemented by fascinating works of sculpture like the marble group in the Great Garden by Pietro Balesta, *Father Time ravishes Beauty*, and the allegorical figures of the Mozart Fountain, *Grace, Youth, and Solemnity*. We spent a day in the picture gallery of the Zwinger Museum. The large circle formed by the buildings and the enclosed garden were particularly impressive. The early German collection was very fine, and an entire room was devoted to the gallery's greatest treasure, Raphael's *Sistine Madonna*.

The next day we took an excursion to the Tharault Valley with its charming forests and streams. We visited the Forestry School there, which we found to be of interest because of the profession of Dorothy's brother, Nick, for whom we purchased a little cane ornament as a memento. Returning to Dresden cold but happy, we strolled along Wiener Strasse to the spacious and attractive Grossen Garten. Before heading for Prague, we took an excursion to Freiburg, where the main attraction is the Romanesque church, the Goldene Pforteam Dom, noted for over eighty figures within the nine arches of the apse.

It was an enchanting experience to travel by train through Saxony on the way to our exit-point from Germany, Bodenbach. The trip took us past so many

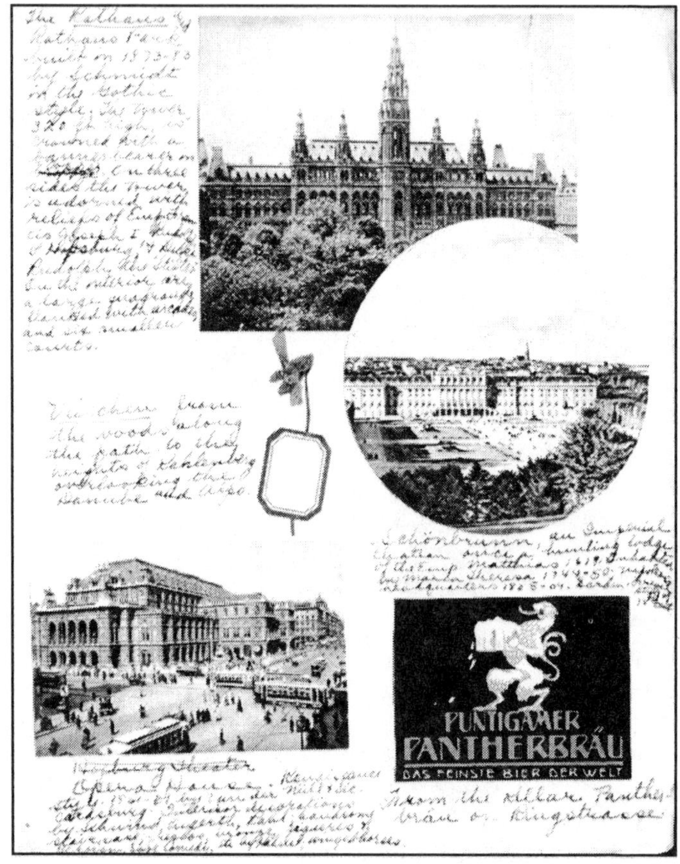

magnificent hills with fortresses, castles, monasteries and churches on their sides, in addition to picturesque villages nestled in the trees and splendid river panoramas. Entering Czechoslovakia, we had a surprise. We had feared that we'd be disappointed after the spectacular scenery of the Elbe

Valley. We could not have been more mistaken. As Dorothy put it in her journal, Czechoslovakia "reminded us of Cumberland Valley. Instead of the Saxony mountains the land extended in rolls and hillocks into more distant hills. The ground was unusually fertile. . . . So it seemed that we had indeed crossed into a new country. . . . From the train window [the countryside] seemed most inviting and fresh, like Switzerland. It never became monotonous."

Czechslovakia became, then, a delightful prelude to Vienna. Prague was a splendid city, and the Staubbach Falls at Lauterbrunneu, plunging from a high, steep cliff, were indeed an arresting sight. We arrived in Vienna very late on the eve of Easter Sunday and spent the first night in a beautiful room decorated in white on the first floor of the Egerlander Hotel. Vienna is a continual feast to the eye and nourishment for the soul. All the splendor, élan, intricacy, and depth of European art, music, sculpture, architecture, and civility seem to be 'condensed' for the visitor in a matchless pattern. Dorothy vividly records our experience of "the spacious streets with trees and bushes beginning to bud and the freshness and lovely architecture of the buildings." The city offered us aesthetic experience in a great variety of forms, from the collection of gems, marble, gold dinner service, and china in the Franz Joseph Palace, to the Art History Museum with masterpieces from almost every school of painting, to the vast four-story rectangle of the Natural History Museum, to the imposing marble staircases of the buildings, and the incredibly rich 'texture' of the Burgtheater. The theater, as Dorothy noted, was adorned by "ceiling paintings in the vestibule and foyer.

The walls of the foyer are decorated with portraits of actors; also paintings in the lunettes & domes. In the sumptuous rooms leading to the imperial boxes the frieze of children & animal figures, the magnificent marble pillars, and the red velvet carpets and hard-wood floors are unparalleled in grandeur."

In addition to the excitements that are usually available to tourists in Vienna, we had a unique opportunity. In the Hoftheater, which is considered one of the most beautiful in the world, from a Royal Box we watched four actors rehearsing a scene for a performance of *Anna Karenina.* The gifts we received, too, from Vienna's natural surroundings entered our hearts forever, and these precious experiences are beautifully rendered in Dorothy's words:

> *Easter Sunday, March 31, 1929. [We] hiked up the steep hill behind the station. Every 'new blick' thru the clearances along the winding path was a new revelation. Finally Vienna appeared and then the Styrian Alps besides the wonderful extent of plains and hills and 'Blue Danube'. The sunset was beautiful the summit was mysterious with the old church and monastery wall and the evening air was cold. The increasing darkness, deep woods close at hand, scattered lights & lights of Vienna afar, the dark outline of the Danube, the neighboring hillside of poles entwined by grape vines bewitched the road of our descent.*

On the train from Vienna to Trieste, our hearts were warmed by a group of Polish university students on a "Studenten Reise," who greeted everyone in the coach with a handshake, singing songs and cheering. At the station where they departed for Belgrade, they gave us a farewell shout, and several students even gave us their cards, which Dorothy pasted in her journal.

Coming off the train in Trieste, we saw for the first time groups of 'Black Shirts', evidencing Mussolini's increasing power. One group came aboard the train and confiscated all the newspapers. Walking along the harbor, I snapped a picture of a Fascisti. In fact, the 'Black Shirts' were eager to be photographed, and one of them even hurried after us to give us his address! Strolling outside Trieste, we were captivated by the superb view of the hillside and harbor with a great variety of ships, white-washed cottages facing the sea, and women who were urging on donkeys pulling milk-carts. We also came upon battlefield signs—shell craters and the rubble of buildings.

In Venice we stayed at the Hotel Rialto on the Grand Canal near the Ponte di Rialto. Just think, we were staying in Shylock's Rialto where bartering was still going on! "In a gondola we took a strolla" past the grand old palaces of Venetian nobility and buildings where Byron and Browning had stayed. Everywhere in Venice the eye is uplifted by a great variety of sights—the arches of the Doges' palaces, the high campanile, the commercial arcades, bobbing anchored or traveling gondolas, the sublime Basilica of San Marco, with four antique bronze horses over the main portal.

Moving from the grand canal into narrow

waterways, our slim vessel took us past residences close on either side, their walls—rising straight from the water—embellished with vines and trellises of flowers. At other points gardens with urns and flower-beds reached to the water's edge.

The Cathedral of San Marco is designed in the form of a Byzantine cross crowned by five domes, lavishly decorated, with mosaics, paintings, and statues in excellent condition. Crossing the threshold through the main entrance, the visitor is overcome with dazzlement and awe, entering into a wholly new domain of experience. In turn, as we moved on to Florence, we were overpowered by the immense façade of the Pitti Palace, as well as the dome and bell-tower of the Florence Cathedral.

Our twelve days in Rome (April 10-22) were even more enjoyable than we anticipated. We did not press ourselves but savored the experience at our leisure, poking

about, living, and loafing in the 'eternal city'. We spent a day in the forum, sat many hours in the Coliseum, and read Gibbon in the Picio Gardens. I was especially fascinated by the Appian Way and our viewing of the Catacombs. As Dorothy put it, the "walk from Tivoli to Hadrian's Villa was a fine mingling of self with environment." Our crowning experience of literary shrines was a morning spent in the Protestant Cemetery that was for Dorothy the fulfillment of a dream. We walked in meditation through the beautiful grounds, the graves full of flowers and marked by many fine monuments, finally reverently following the path from the Shelley memorial to Keats's grave.

Unfolding in tandem with our pilgrimage into the European world of history and the arts, my work with the famed Max Bodenstein, Director of the Physical-Chemical Institute of the University of Berlin, would prove to have a life-long impact on my development as a scientist. In mid-September, 1928, I began my research in Bodenstein's lab. My initial inquiry into the trimolecular mechanism, however, didn't progress satisfactorily, so I took up a project involving the possibility of a magnetic field effect on the gas reaction of carbon monoxide with oxygen. After many months, no substantial effect was found, perhaps because magnets available at the time were not sufficiently strong.

In contrast to these unsuccessful projects, Bodenstein was continuing his pioneering experiments on the reaction of hydrogen with chlorine to give hydrochloric acid:

$$H_2 + Cl_2 \rightarrow 2HCl$$

At the University of Hannover earlier in his career he had postulated a mechanism involving formation of a reactive species in one step that was regenerated in subsequent steps. For example, the light-induced ($h\nu$) reaction occurs by such a process:

$$Cl_2 + h\nu \rightarrow 2Cl$$

$$Cl + H_2 \rightarrow HCl + H$$

$$H + Cl_2 \rightarrow HCl + Cl$$

After many repeat cycles, in which an initially formed Cl atom, a very reactive free radical, produces new Cl, the process is terminated by:

$Cl + X \rightarrow ClX$ [where X is H or Cl].

One day while pondering his ideas of getting many repeat cycles out of one reactive species he was thoughtfully fingering his vest watch chain. "Oh," he exclaimed to a graduate student, "This is a '*chain* reaction'!" It was, indeed, a historic moment, the origin of the concept *chain reaction*, which has since played a major role in both science and history. When my son Lance paid a professional visit to the Chemistry Department of the University of Hannover in the 1980's, he mentioned that I had worked with Bodenstein. His host instantly rushed to a safe, returning with a gold watch chain Bodenstein had made to commemorate this event. Just imagine these many decades later, my son holding this powerful symbol in his hands!

In 1928-29, the confluence of pioneering scientific thinkers in Berlin was mind-boggling. Nearby Bodenstein's research institute was a physics-chemistry research facility whose monthly meetings I attended. In the discussions conducted there I heard Erwin Schrödinger and Max Planck contribute, and—would you believe it—Werner Heisenberg and Albert Einstein as well! Someone asked Schrödinger what the wave function meant, and he answered to the effect, why don't we think of its value squared representing the

probability of finding an electron at a certain place. And now that is the *starting point* of our current thinking of electrons around an atom or molecule.

Bodenstein and Strauss, Heisenberg and Keats, Einstein and Wagner , Schrödinger and Scott, the medley goes on and on. How rich and multi-faceted our European odyssey was! Of course, as the academic year wound to a close in Germany, we had to move on to another 'Ithaca'—our upcoming commitments at home. Thus, we embarked in mid-June on the *S.S. Leviathan*, bound from Southampton to New York.

. . . Yield who will to their separation,
My object in living is to unite
My avocation and my vocation
As my two eyes make one in sight.
Only where love and need are one,
And work is play for mortal stakes,
Is the deed ever really done
For Heaven and the future's sakes. . .

Robert Frost
from "Two Tramps in Mud Time"

COLUMBIA UNIVERSITY
New York, New York, 1929-1940

Disembarking in New York, I practically stepped from the gangplank into the classroom, for I began teaching Summer School immediately after our arrival. Subsequent to our return, we felt the impact of the Wall Street crash, which threw the country into turmoil. This was a period when the dependable, if modest, income of an academic kept me immune to the wide-spread economic perils of the time. At Columbia that Fall Semester, I was highly challenged by my teaching. I was offering a new course in Photochemistry concerned with atoms, free radicals, and excited states. These matters were an extension of the Bodenstein neutral atom systems. Throughout the semester I was joined in class sessions by Harold Urey, who had studied at Berkeley, done postdoctoral work with Niels Bohr, taught at Johns Hopkins and had come to Columbia while I was in Europe. The text in the course, *Photochemical Processes*, was by George B. Kistiakowsky of Harvard, who had taken his doctorate with Bodenstein and would later play a key role at Los Alamos, as well as being a White House Science Advisor (Rhodes 1986: 542). In the Photochemistry Course, Urey and I engaged in extensive discussion about the interaction of atoms and molecules with light of various wave lengths and energies. Two graduate students from the Bio-Physics area also made a strong contribution. One of them, George Wald—later at Harvard—was to receive a Nobel Prize for the chemistry of vision. The other, Jacinto Steinhardt, would be awarded the Congressional Medal of Freedom for anti-submarine technology. In view of the fact that Harold Urey was to receive the Nobel Prize for his work on Deuterium, this was truly a high-powered scientific gathering! Can you imagine how late I stayed up on Sunday evenings to prepare for this

class? Remember, these concepts were still in their infancy.

The course in photochemistry was a major interest for me over the years at Columbia, and it has been rewarding to learn that my students continued to be inspired by it. Thus, I was delighted, for example, to receive from Sidney W. Benson, who received many national awards, the following dedication in his book, *Thermochemical Kinetics* (Wiley, 1976): "To Ray Crist, Whose course in photochemistry in 1937 at Columbia opened up a new world of chemistry to an eager undergraduate, 30 years after the historic experiments of Lind & Bodenstein and before the first textbook in photochemistry. It was an exciting period in science with a warm and enthusiastic guide. It made a deep impression on me which has never left." This is the sort of appreciation which indeed confirms a teacher's hope that his classes offer something worthwhile to the world of science.

As joint-author of the book (with A.E. Ruark), *Protons, Molecules, and Quanta*, Harold Urey asked me to join him in checking the proofs. This work represented his 'Physics' interpretation of Chemistry, which was very different from the prevailing point of view at Columbia. He established, moreover, *The Journal of Chemical Physics*, of which I was an associate editor. Of considerable interest to me also was my supervision of the undergraduate Inorganic Chemistry laboratory. Over 125 students were guided by twelve graduate assistants. The routine experiments were not stimulating, and I had difficulty keeping both students and assistants stimulated by the work. I realized that what was lacking in this lab, and in its conventional manual, was sparking of the student's imaginative, individual contribution. Working with students, I therefore proceeded to set up a situation in which they would devise their own experimental approaches leading to unique results. Thus, they would participate in the creative process and cultivate an affinity with thc chcmical world. With thcsc frcsh experiences, the lab assistants were as engaged as the students. Eventually, this approach came to fruition in a lab manual, which was published by McGraw-Hill in 1941.

At the time, my work in the laboratory concerned the reaction $2NO + O_2 \rightarrow 2NO_2$. This was considered to be a trimolecular reaction with three molecules coming together in one collision. However, my ground-breaking discoveries showed it to be a sequence of two bimolecular reactions via a reactive intermediate, in this case, NO_3:

$$NO + O_2 \rightarrow NO_3$$

$$NO_3 + NO \rightarrow 2NO_2$$

This conclusion is one now generally found, or assumed, by later researchers for many systems. Anyone who has ever tried to get three busy people in a room for a meeting at one time knows how hard it is, while getting only two active people together is much easier! Another area of my investigations involved findings on the photochemical decomposition of potassium persulfate, showing that one quantum of light causes one molecule to react. This fundamental conclusion as well is one now generally assumed by others studying photochemical reactions. Pursuing phenomena in the laboratory, gathering data to demonstrate a hypothesis, and working the data into effective presentation for publication were activities that were deeply satisfying to me. Nature had offered me the opportunity to probe her workings, to clarify and communicate her wonders. I couldn't imagine a more gratifying and ceaselessly challenging way of life.

During these years, I also joined Leonard Smidth, an organic chemist, in producing a plastic material we called Aldure, which was used as a window glass substitute, or could be exploited to produce a variety of useful things. Smitty and I had roomed together during my early years of graduate study, and he had been working in a Philadelphia company for several years. When he came back to Columbia and later ran a lab in a small chemical company operating near Brooklyn Bridge, I collaborated with him, and we secured a patent for Aldure in 1932. As it turned out, that lab also proved to be important in the life of Dorothy's sister, Vira, who was studying literature at Barnard College of Columbia University and living with us in Grantwood. Through me, she got a part-time secretary's job in Smitty's company. A charming, energetic young fellow by the name of Fritz Anderson also happened to be employed there. Thus, Fritz and Vira met, and it was love at first sight!

At the time, another exciting event for the Lenhart family—and all of us— was the literary work that Dorothy's father was doing about life in their small Pennsylvania town. DeLance Lenhart's portrait of doings in New Cumberland began as a four-page autobiographical sketch, entitled "My Town," which appeared in *Scribner's Magazine* (September, 1929). This issue of the prestigious periodical also contained an installment of Hemingway's *A Farewell to Arms* as well as "Charles Chaplin: A Portrait" by the noted critic and novelist Waldo Frank. Squire Lenhart's work had been praised by Robert Bridges, the English poet laureate, who was on the editorial board of the magazine. Bridges said that he was sorry to ask the author to cut some pages from "My Town" so that *Scribner's Magazine* could publish it. "It has been a pleasure to read 'My Town'," Bridges writes. "It is written with appreciation of the character and quality and lure of life in a small town" (letter to the author, 3-13-29). Also, as DeLance Lenhart states in a letter of January, 1930, to Dorothy and Vira, a reviewer in the *Raleigh News* was of the opinion that "I am right up there . . . with Sinclair [Lewis] or even truer to life than his pictures." This praise, along with his family's appreciation of his writing, inspired the ailing Justice-of-the Peace to press on with writing. Between January 30, 1930 and August 4, 1930—the time of his death—he expanded his brief but vivid magazine narrative into a full presentation. "The more I think of it," he writes with humorous bravado to his daughters, anticipating his project, "why couldn't I spread the thing out with anecdotes into a book 'My Town' since I can depict it truer than [Lewis's] Main Street? [I would] start out as I did coming here forty years ago when I was 10 and using the pranks of boyhood, incidents of the town, methods of small town politics, justice-of-the peace happenings, and general doings such as the stories [of veterans about the Civil War]..."

Indeed, the sketch "My Town" did grow into book length, but the ninety-nine page manuscript did not come to light until Vira Lenhart Anderson happened upon it in her father's papers and typed several copies. Ross W. Lenhart published his grandfather's work in 1978 with its extended title: *My Town: An Autobiography of the author and an account of the town he grew up with.* Finally, one more word about the Lenharts at the time should be included. On the back of her husband's one-page letter to his daughters, Dorothy's mother, Clara, wrote her own page of greetings in which she warmly thanked them for their letters home. So encouraging and loving were these letters that they invigorated the afflicted writer: "He is all interested [in writing] again," Clara wrote, "[and] seems to have taken on new life." Up to the time of his death, DeLance Lenhart was collecting materials which, had he lived on, would no doubt have led to additional publications. For example, in one of his personal essays, "Fraidy-Cat," he recalls a grim story of the battlefield told by his son-in-law Douglas Beidel. Just as Hemingway had served in Italy, Doug had served as an ambulance driver in France. Rarely, however, could he bring himself to reveal his experiences. "My son-in-law," DeLance Lenhart writes, "tells of the time he crowded into a dug-out and stole the blanket off three fellows to keep warm. When he woke up in the morning he found the men had been dead for weeks."

I must add that as the young scientist in the family, I was not exempt from my father-in-law's satire, as he poked fun in "Fraidy-Cat" at my preoccupation with laboratory investigation: "My son-in-law [Ray] will see everything from a scientific point of view and argue on the chemical reaction and prove it by analysis. The piece of pipe [Dorothy and he came upon in France] and found to be a revolver . . . he will work on . . .in the lab for some time. But he will submit a lengthy report to prove by runs that there was a war and we will know all about a revolver that was partly buried on the battlefield . . . for eleven years. . .". I heard a lot of lively stories directly from Squire Lenhart, and I was inspired by Dorothy and Vira's messages to their dad both boosting his morale and activating his 'chemistry' of literary creativity.

As for the product Smitty and I developed at the time, nothing much came of that. The sole remnants of Aldure were a couple of elegant mechanical pencils that I used through the 1950's. Nonetheless, production of plastic does fit into the pattern of my activities in industry which at Carbide were to involve polymers in a big way. Another side effort in New York at the time was the use of activated charcoal as a filter for tobacco. Occasionally I smoked a pipe, and I found that a bit of activated charcoal at the bottom of the bowl provided a useful filter to trap tars and other substances. With this in mind, I worked up a charcoal filter for cigarettes, finding that a company in New York was interested in promoting that filter for commercial cigarette production. This was a promising prospect, but its continuance was eventually blocked by the beginning of the war.

At Columbia, significant things were happening in research. Harold Urey was on the cutting edge of discovery, and we were inspired by his always restless, dynamic investigations. He was involved in pioneering work concerning isotope reactions. In a Physics meeting in Washington, D.C., he met with a group from the National Bureau of Standards who were trying to understand the abnormal low temperature effect of hydrogen, thinking it might be an atomic structure phenomenon. They then supplied him with residual hydrogen from a low temperature vaporization. He set out to examine hydrogen wave lengths of samples obtained over a vaporization range. The samples on excitation had a weak line associated with each of the several hydrogen lines. The position of these weak lines was

predicted by Urey assuming an isotope of hydrogen that was twice as heavy. Thus, Urey discovered heavy hydrogen, which he named 'Deuterium'. He then became extremely active in working on hydrogen systems to find a Deuterium enhancement process, and I joined in the effort. After months, a California scientist, G.N. Lewis, reported enriched Deuterium concentrations in the electrolysis process. Urey's inquiry gained momentum and for his achievement he was awarded the Nobel Prize. These developments in science, combined with dramatic events in history, were preparing for unforeseeable dimensions in the history of our time.

University of Chicago scientists who were instrumental in the development of the atomic bomb gathered for luncheon to open the Institute of Nuclear Studies and Institute of Metals at the University.

Standing, left to right: Edward Teller; T. Hogness; Walter Zinn; Clarence Zener; Joselph E. Mayer; Philip W. Schultz; R.H. Crist of Columbia U.; and Carl Eckhart, University of California.

Seated, left to right: W.H. Zachariasen; Harold C. Urey; Cyril Smith, Director of Metals Institute, Enrico Fermi; and Samuel K. Allison, Director of Nuclear Studies Institute.

Tyger! Tyger! Burning bright
In the forests of the night,
What immortal hand or eye
Could frame thy fearful symmetry?

In what distant deeps or skies
Burnt the fire of thine eyes?
On what wings dare he aspire?
What the hand dare seize the fire?

And what shoulder, & what art,
Could twist the sinews of thy heart?
And when thy heart began to beat,
What dread hand? & what dread feet?

What the hammer? what the chain
In what furnace was thy brain?
What the anvil? what dread grasp
Dare its deadly terrors clasp?

When the stars threw down their spears,
And watered heaven with their tears,
Did he smile his work to see?
Did he who made the lamb make thee?

Tyger! Tyger! burning bright
In the forests of the night,
What immortal hand or eye,
Dare frame thy fearful symmetry?

William Blake
"The Tyger"
from Songs of Experience

THE MANHATTAN PROJECT
New York, New York, 1941-1945

In 1938, a discovery took place in Germany which profoundly affected the future of mankind. Two analytical chemists, Otto Hahn and Fritz Strassmann, were puzzled by the presence of Barium in Uranium that had been subjected to neutron bombardment. It could not be interpreted as an inorganic impurity. Hahn wrote to physicist Lise Meitner about this strange discovery. To avoid Nazi persecution, she had fled first to Denmark, where Niels Bohr arranged for a position in Sweden for her. In his letter to Meitner, Hahn asked her to think of some explanation of his discovery. On Christmas day, she and her physicist nephew Otto Frisch, who had come to Sweden from Denmark for the holidays, conceived of the idea that the Uranium nucleus captured a neutron, and then the nucleus split into two fragments, releasing a huge amount of energy (Rhodes: 257-259).

Frisch returned to Copenhagen and told Niels Bohr their idea. Bohr "struck his forehead with his hand, and exclaimed, 'Oh what idiots we have all been! But this is wonderful'" (Rhodes: 261). On Jan. 6, three days later, Bohr sailed for New York. Then, on Jan. 13, Frisch got experimental evidence of those fragments. He asked a microbiologist present that day, "What do you call the process in which one bacterium divides into two?" and got the answer "binary fission." With that, Frisch coined the term 'fission' for nuclear disintegration (Rhodes: 262-264). Word of the Hahn-Meitner results spread like wildfire. A major leak occurred, for example, when Bohr told his shipboard colleague Rosenfeld, who—not realizing it was to be confidential until the Hahn and Meitner papers were published—told a Princeton physics discussion group.

On Jan. 16, Bohr was met at the New York dock by Nobel Prize Laureate Enrico Fermi and his wife, Laura. Fermi had recently come to Columbia University, fleeing fascist persecution in Italy. Fermi aided Bohr in practical affairs in New York, and on Jan. 25 the Danish scientist went to Columbia to discuss fission with Fermi. Fermi was not in his office, but Bohr then gave full information to Herbert Anderson, a colleague of Fermi's. That evening Anderson performed an experiment which Fermi had asked him to do earlier in the day, and that experiment confirmed that Uranium splits into fragments.

In Princeton, on Feb. 5, Bohr had the sudden insight that U^{235} is the isotope that absorbs slow neutrons and leads to fission. He had been at dinner with colleagues when he abruptly left, going silently to his office in the Institute for Advanced Study. There he wrote down and explained his reasoning. The possibility of a chain reaction involving neutrons for Uranium fission had been mentioned by Szilard as early as 1934 in patent application for nuclear energy (Rhodes: 203-204, 214-216) and later in terms of its destructive power (Rhodes: 266-268) . Experiments by Joliot in France and a week later by Szilard at Columbia showed that about two neutrons were emitted for one absorbed so that an *explosive* chain reaction might be possible. Separation of the reactive U^{235} from U^{238} became the crucial difficult goal. Szilard had said that "it might take five to ten years before it could be done on a technical scale" (Rhodes: 289). Bohr's skepticism about producing nuclear energy, according to John Wheeler, concerned the "enormous difficulty of separating the necessary quantities of U^{235}." Fermi noted in a lecture that it was by no means evident in 1939 that the task of separating large amounts of U^{235} was feasible. Teller remembered that at a Princeton meeting Bohr had insisted, "It can never be done unless you turn the whole United States into one huge factory" (Rhodes: 294).

At Columbia University, therefore, the separation of the isotopes became an enormously challenging priority. Urey received funds from the Department of the Navy to pursue separation of the isotopes. He and his colleagues worked in secret for months trying to make a filter, or barrier, to separate U^{235} from U^{238} as their gaseous uranium fluorides, UF_6. The idea was that lighter molecules containing U^{235} would travel faster and diffuse through the filter more easily. However, a workable filter seemed beyond their grasp. This impasse, which had thrown the researchers into despair, was overcome by an unforeseen event. British scientists working on their own gaseous diffusion method of separating Uranium isotopes had likewise been trying to find a suitable barrier for separation of the isotopes. Someone there thought of trying something like the wire screen in the

Lectromesh paint sprayer (!) and approached its inventor, an interior decorator named Ed Norris living in Connecticut. Imagine Norris's surprise when Franz Simon from England appeared one day and asked him to make a half-inch square screen with a half-million holes in it! Before long, Norris took two very promising samples to my colleague Dunning at Columbia. Shock gave way to amazement as we tested the material—and lo and behold, it worked! At last we had the breakthrough everyone was anxiously awaiting.

Dunning, Urey, Fermi, and I (among a small circle of Columbia scientists) were shaken—as were our colleagues at Princeton and elsewhere—by the prospect of the military potential of the atomic chain reaction in which reactive neutrons released in one step 'recycle' to cause further reactions. In the phenomenon of an explosion from an atomic chain reaction, we were confronted with potential for an astounding weapon—the unprecedented destructive power of a Uranium bomb; and we were also cognizant of the appalling possibility that German scientists might be pressing to develop this knowledge for military purposes.

It was in the light of these discoveries in areas that were being investigated both in Europe and the United States that Albert Einstein wrote a historic letter to President Franklin D. Roosevelt, encouraging the President to support research on nuclear fission. On August 2, 1939, (as quoted by Libby, 1979), Einstein wrote Roosevelt from Nassau Point, Long Island, "In the course of the last four months it has been made possible—through the work of Joliot in France as well as Fermi and Szilard in America—that it may become possible to set up a nuclear chain reaction in a large mass of uranium, by which vast amounts of power . . . would be generated. . . . This new phenomenon would also lead to the construction of bombs, and it is conceivable—though much less certain—that extremely powerful bombs of a new type may thus be constructed. . . . . In view of this situation you may think it desirable to have some permanent contact between the Administration and the group of physicists working on chain reactions in America."

Thus, military pressures and scientific efforts led to the top-secret crash program of research and development, the Manhattan District Project, set up with General Leslie Groves as engineering director of the nationwide effort. Groves, who was famous as supervisor of the construction of the Pentagon, was a sound choice for managing the technical operations of the Manhattan Project, which involved—besides our laboratories—facilities primarily at the University of Chicago, Oak Ridge (Tennessee), Hanford (Washington), and Los Alamos (New Mexico). Harold Urey was appointed scientific director of the Columbia University effort, and in 1941, I too went on leave from Columbia to join the Project.

Between December 1941 and April 1942, Fermi went back and forth between Columbia University and the University of Chicago. Thereafter he remained with the Chicago group and supervised the first uranium chain reaction, which took place in a converted squash court (dubbed the 'Metallurgical Laboratory') under the football stands at Stagg Field.

ON DECEMBER 2, 1942
MAN ACHIEVED HERE
THE FIRST SELF-SUSTAINING CHAIN REACTION
AND THEREBY INITIATED THE
CONTROLLED RELEASE OF NUCLEAR ENERGY

Laura Fermi calls this commemorative plaque on the stands of Stagg Field 'the birth certificate of the atomic era' (1954: ix). In a sense it was also the scientific birth certificate of all of us on the Manhattan Project who worked so furiously and creatively pursuing the processes of nuclear fission. It is impossible to exaggerate the excitement and pressure under which developments unfolded. Work at Columbia—and at all Project locations—proceeded with such secrecy that not even spouses were permitted to fathom the nature of our unprecedented mission. The only information Laura Fermi had, for example, was that "there were no metallurgists at the Metallurgical Laboratory" (176), and all Dorothy knew was that I was working on a complex, urgent project in collaboration with many leading scientists.

Initially, dozens of men in the Columbia group were involved in the quest for a suitable barrier for separation of the Uranium isotopes. Corrosion of the barrier was a major problem. Bill Libby had learned critical information about the chemistry of UF_6 and the corrosive rates of various materials, as well as those that might resist corrosion, such as fluorocarbons. Another invaluable contribution made by Bill Libby (known to some as 'Wild Bill') was to 'tame' the extremely reactive fluorine to condition all components that would come in contact with the extremely corrosive UF_6. The scientists were dealing with complex problems under great pressure to achieve their goal as soon as possible. Time was so precious on the Project that, for example, instead of working out mass production methods Dobie Keith of Kellex proposed that the final steps be done by large numbers of employees doing piecework. So intense was the effort to maximize the pace of the Project's effort that the gigantic Oak Ridge diffusion plant was built *before* we had the barrier. Even a picture of the plant cannot adequately express its size—half a mile long, the roof covering 42.6 acres (Rhodes: 220).

Enormous efforts led to progress in Project laboratories around the country. On one occasion, in 1944 as I recall, I had occasion to go with a scientist from Columbia to consult with the amazing thinker whom I had

seen in Berlin—Albert Einstein. We visited Einstein at his modest home in Princeton. My fellow visitor discussed extensively details of a Washington meeting that Einstein had attended. I exchanged thoughts more briefly with him about the question of the atomic bomb. I was deeply impressed by the German genius's quiet, gentle manner. Though he was at the forefront of developments in twentieth century physics and mathematics—a legendary figure—he was unassuming, and his openness to others was truly inspiring.

It was phenomenal that in spite of the geographical spread of our research efforts, effective co-ordination was achieved. At one point, General Groves, in his overall supervisory capacity, had set up an extensive laboratory building at Oak Ridge expressly intended as a working center for the entire scientific team. The scientists, however, insisted on staying put in their individual home territories. Groves's intense frustration from his carefully planned, costly, but thwarted effort to increase project security as well as efficiency was shown on a later occasion when a group of scientists presented him with a sheaf of blueprints for a production facility. "What's the Nobel factor?" the general snapped, referring to the vagaries of genius which he had repeatedly encountered in the scientific staff. He was informed that no Nobel winners were involved in the planning. "Very well!" he said. "Let us proceed!"

Given the political complexities of the world in 1945, the ferocity of the war in the Pacific, the military exigency of using the atomic bomb, and the tragic repercussions of its use, it is no wonder that the Project scientists were divided on the question of its use. Scientists, of course, did not interfere in the political—and ultimately presidential—decision on the issue. Nevertheless, as everyone knows we were divided—for the most part silently—among themselves. It seemed that there were fewer conflicts at Columbia, while at Chicago there were more doubts about the advisability of dropping the bomb, as there were at Los Alamos, though even the doubters worked whole-heartedly toward the achievement of a national goal. So, dedication was in some cases strangely blended with hesitancy. For example Kistiakowsky (whom I never met personally, though I admired his writing), had to be insistently wooed by Groves and Oppenheimer in 1943 to join the team at Los Alamos, and he said—as quoted by Rhodes (542)—that this gave him "a wonderful opportunity to act as a reluctant bride throughout the project."

As history records, we pressed forward through all challenges and confusions to the earth-shaking culmination of the Project. In 1944, Urey made the decision to leave the Columbia group and join Fermi and others in setting up a nuclear research institute at the University of Chicago. Thereupon, I was appointed director of the Manhattan Project, Columbia group, beginning January, 1945. While our group's mission was achieved, the scientific staff was still hard at work examining the knowledge we had gained and providing consultation for those who were working at the various locations around the country. The mandate which I received upon taking over was to coordinate the work of our investigators so as to minimize friction between sometimes sensitive or opposed temperaments, and maximize the dynamic interplay of talents. I was grateful that I was considered to be one who could communicate with all concerned, 'mending fences' and 'building bridges', for stimulating both individual efforts and creative interaction was exactly the role which I had always striven to embrace.

The war in Europe ended in May, 1945, and allied forces focused on massive engagement in the Pacific theater. The first atomic bomb was assembled at Los Alamos and was successfully tested at Trinity site near Almagordo air base on July 16, 1945. The following month, on vacation, at a neighbor's home near my father's farm in Grantham, Pennsylvania, I heard over the radio the first dramatic news bulletin announcing that an atomic bomb had been dropped on Hiroshima. Three days later an atomic bomb fell on Nagasaki. Soon thereafter, my heart sank once more as I witnessed in newsreels the awesome spectacle of the mushroom cloud towering above the scene of unprecedented devastation. The rationale for its use, in my mind, was the saving of up to an estimated three million American and Japanese lives had an invasion of the Japanese homeland occurred.

During the course of our labors, the war effort had spurred us to complete our mission, fearful of the consequences of failure. At the same time, the 'unthinkable'—the use of such a 'doomsday' weapon—weighed heavily on our minds. We never knew whether the weapon would in fact be used. Its deployment, as noted, was a political-military decision, yet our very own thirst for scientific knowledge and concerted technological effort had brought the bomb into the world.

The Evening News

HARRISBURG, PENNA., FRIDAY, AUGUST 10, 1945

Former Student at Little Grantham School Had Major Role in Atomic Bomb Work

Shown above is the "little red schoolhouse," near Grantham, where Dr. Ray Henry Crist, who played a major part in development of the atomic bomb, received his early education. Doctor Crist is shown below grasping the knob of the school's door.

A man who was born and bred in the upper part of Cumberland County and received his fundamental training in "a little red schoolhouse," near Grantham, had an important part in the development of the atomic bomb, it was revealed here today.

The scientist is Dr. Ray Henry Crist, son of Mr. and Mrs. Henry Crist, Mechanicsburg, R. D. 2, who is director of one of the several major research laboratories responsible for the bomb that is expected to bring World War II to a sudden conclusion.

Doctor Crist, who is associate professor of chemistry at Columbia University, has been on leave of absence since January 1, 1942. He served for two years as director of laboratories under Dr. H. C. Urey, who was chief of a Columbia University Division of the Office of Scientific Research and Development, prior to being made director of the research laboratory he now heads.

Doctor Crist received his early training in a one-room red brick school known as Center Square School in Upper Allen Township, Cumberland County, about a mile from Grantham, later attended Grantham College, and was graduated from Dickinson College in 1920 with an A. B. degree.

He received the degree of doctor of philosophy at Columbia University in 1926 and has been a member of the faculty of the university since that time.

He has written a laboratory manual in chemistry and is the author of a number of publications in the field of reactions of gases and properties of heavy hydrogen and heavy water.

With his wife and three small sons he spent a week at the Crist homestead one mile south of Shepherdstown, returning to New York City yesterday.

On Wednesday he walked back to the little red school house that he attended as a boy, and gazed with admiration at the giant oak tree that spreads its sheltering bough over the small red brick building where he learned his three Rs.

The New York scientist told of the many times he and his brother, Dr. Guy C. Crist, local physician, had "shinnied up that tree" when they were boys.

He believed that development of the atomic bomb will lead to extensive research in the general field for many years to come.

. . . I doubt not through the ages one increasing
purpose runs,
And the thoughts of men are widened with the
process of the suns.

What is that to him that reaps not harvest of his
youthful joys,
Though the deep heart of existence beat forever
like a boy's?

Alfred Tennyson
from "Locksley Hall"

FAMILY LIFE DURING THE WAR YEARS
Leonia, New Jersey

While science and history were bent on their problematic course, our family life was unfolding in new dimensions of growth and love. In 1936, Dorothy and I moved to a home in Leonia, New Jersey. As it turned out, both the Ureys and the Fermis also came to live in Leonia. We enjoyed their friendship, and for years Harold and I commuted together to the city. As we drove to and fro, we held our tongues concerning issues on the Project, since another person was present—a Columbia colleague from the Political Science Department! In our commuting trips, then, Harold and I usually just chatted about everyday matters, but there were times that—without revealing the source of his preoccupation—he was thrown into a taciturn or volatile mood. An incident occurred which illustrated the situation of which the third commuter was unaware. We were in my car picking him up for the morning commute. I don't recall that it was an especially nerve-wracking moment on the Project; in any case, Harold was tense and anxious to get to the city. We found, however, that our colleague was light-heartedly romping with his dog on the lawn of his home, and did not wish at once to take his seat in the car. As he continued for some moments in carefree play with his pet, I felt Harold's irritation mounting. He said nothing, but when we arrived in Manhattan he slammed the car door with such vehemence that the window shattered!

Over the years, my pleasant and rewarding friendship and collaboration with Harold Urey repeatedly confirmed for me both the effectiveness of our work together and the differences in our personalities. He was the demanding leader and I was the patient organizer. He was the intuitive genius and I was the painstaking researcher. He was the aggressive challenger and I was the persistent peacemaker. He owned a swank Pierce-Arrow automobile and built a stone mansion, while I was content with our used Ford and comfortable bungalow. He was a Nobel Laureate, while I could only claim to be the teacher and supporter of Nobel laureates.

During the war period, our home at 30 Glenwood Avenue was a haven where I tried to escape the pressures and worries of the Project. In August, 1938, our family life received a great boon. We had long wanted to enrich our lives with children, but unfortunately Dorothy had suffered two miscarriages. We welcomed the alternative of adoption, and after an elaborate application process and several visits to a Manhattan agency, a seventeen month old child—Robert—came into our life. When we first approached his crib at the agency's nursery, we were delighted and moved by his reaching his arms out to us. Our home in Leonia was now filled with the beauties of new life and parenting. Our little boy grew with leaps and bounds, and before long he was running around the house. Furthermore, we learned in February, 1940, that he would not be an only child! Dorothy was an expectant mother! In July, I was teaching a summer course in analytical chemistry. In the middle of a lecture to a large class I was surprised by an urgent summons: "Professor Crist, you must go at once to Presbyterian

Hospital on 168th Street!"

Rushing to Dorothy's hospital room, what did I find but the *three* of them—the joyous mother and adorable twins! I learned that Robert's bumping into Dorothy had triggered premature delivery. Hastening to the hospital, Dorothy gave birth to a son and lay back with relief. But no—it wasn't over! "Mrs. Crist," said the astonished doctor, "you have another child!" The twin boys were around five pounds, and they were cared for in incubators for five weeks. There was some apprehension that since one twin, Lance, was only four and a half pounds, he might experience some complications, but that turned out to be a false alarm.

The unexpected pair were tagged Baby A and Baby B by the nursing staff, since Dorothy and I were only prepared with a boy's or girl's name. Dorothy and her sisters engaged in a lively debate concerning appropriate alternatives for two boys' names. I intervened with the idea that the twins should take names derived from both grandparents on the two sides of the family. Dorothy enthusiastically agreed. We decided that Baby A would be named Henry Spera Crist, namesake of my father and mother; and Baby B would be DeLanson Ross Crist, namesake of Dorothy's parents (Ross was her mother's maiden name; Dorothy's maiden name—Lenhart—had become Robert's middle name).

Then it was home to Leonia. And now you found me, a baby on each knee, giving the tiny fellows their formula with bottles held in crossed hands. Dorothy and I were up nights, with a feeding at six A.M., and then I was on my way to the city. The routine was exhausting, but friends and relatives were soon there to aid in nurturing three sons.

There was nothing sweeter than watching Dorothy joyously care for the babies and guide Robert in his relations with his brothers. In 1943 Henry and Lance were delightful little blond-haired toddlers. With his blond hair, Robert and the twins made a cute trio as he would pull them along in his wagon or play with them at the seashore. At the time when the twins were not as yet ambulatory, I was able—as they say nowadays—to spend some 'quality time' with Robert. In the woods by our Leonia neighborhood, there was a brook. I created a small pond where he floated his boat. This nook in the woods was our special world. I will never forget the little boat floating on clear water reflecting the leaves of surrounding trees. Robert also liked to go with me to our 'victory garden' in a plot by Grand Avenue. It was wonderful, as he looked on with curiosity, to get my hands once more into the earth and watch the plants spring up. Another 'hobby' I shared was 'wood-working'. I crafted a velvet-lined jewel case for Dorothy, having Robert feel the grain and see the effects of various grades of sandpaper. Life in our home was indeed a world apart from the pressure of

the Project and news of the war. We often attended services in Manhattan's Riverside Church nearby Columbia University. As I recall, this church was nominally Baptist, but its pastor, Harry Emerson Fosdick, Professor at Union Theological Seminary, attracted a diverse congregation. Fosdick's famous sermons were broadcast nationally, and we sometimes listened to them over the radio. On one occasion, when we were tuned in to a broadcast of war news, Robert said, "Switch the station to the Reverend Fosdick, and we won't have war any more!"

Another incident involved all three boys and Dorothy. One day when Robert was in his second-grade class on an upper floor of the school, he looked out the window, and what did he see but his mother and four year old Henry on the fire-escape! Dorothy had come to school for some reason and had the twins on harnesses. One moment Henry somehow slipped away and with amazing agility crawled right up the fire-escape. Dorothy attached Lance's harness to the bottom of the stairs and swiftly caught up with Henry. It was at that time that Robert and his mother looked with surprise at one another through the classroom window. An hour later, as Dorothy and the three boys were on their way home, Robert spoke severely to Dorothy: "Mother, you did something naughty! When school started at the beginning of the year, my teacher told us we should *never, never* play on the fire-escape!"

During a war, children who are not in the war zone fortunately experience violence only from a distance. No one close to us at the time was a victim of Second World War violence, though later it turned out that Henry's father-in-law, Glenn Heberlig, was marked for life by the bloodshed that he had experienced as a veteran at the Battle of the Bulge. As it turned out, he was one of the thousands of the Japan invasion fleet who were spared the horrors of mutilation or death by the dropping of the atomic bombs. All that our boys knew about the war during the conflict was what they heard on the news or on radio programs of one kind or another. When the war closed, the boys put red-white-and blue bunting on their bicycles and marched in the Victory Day Parade. Another memorable event for the family was the passing of the United States fleet along the Hudson River, which we viewed from high above on the cliffs of Palisade Park. The panorama of the ships' stately

passage along the river as far as the eye could see was enormously powerful and breathtakingly unforgettable. But war's end brought, too, images of horror which could never be erased from memory. Newsreels showed numerous scenes from concentration camps. Dorothy and I viewed them aghast, noting that Robert, who was old enough to come along to the movies, was clearly affected by the appalling reality with which we were confronted.

This was the time, in 1946, that Harriet Repplier Boyd, whose studio was also in Leonia, did a group

portrait of the boys—a memento of their childhood and of that period in our lives. That portrait hangs in my living room side by side with other items coming down from the past: —for example, a pendulum clock (one of my father's post-auction acquisitions); a maple coffee table Robert built in high school shop in South Charleston; an impressionist painting of the covered bridge near the Messiah campus, done by Zdenka Horak; and Henry's striking photograph of a church dome overlooking the spectacular bay of the famous Greek Island of Santorini. The group portrait of the boys, entitled 'Lanny, Robert & Henry', marked our final year in Leonia. In the post-war period, sweeping changes were coming about in the world; and, likewise, our family entered a new phase of development in a new setting.

I first understood
the texture of wood
as I followed your hands
sanding the side
of a velvet-lined jewelry box,
a gift you made for mother.

I understood, too, the versatility
of hands, as you set
row on row of beans and flowers
in the Victory Garden. . .
and tuned the Bunsen Burner
to blow glass in South Charleston.

I admit that simply watching
it was hard to keep up
with hands constructing
model molecules with
plastic sticks and rubber balls,

hands that gave a hand
with Lance's first, as it were,
Rube Goldberg machine,
a wind tunnel, I guess,
powered by an old
tank vacuum cleaner;
hands that with finesse
set before Hank
his first microscope,
fitted with the camera's eye-
those hands a sign
of the heart's love
of diversity, in a house
where mother's violin
sounded the feminine note,

and you could see
in her eyes the days
of lectures by Carl Van Doren
and matinees at the Met,

or standing room
in the opera of Berlin
before the world
was taught the holocaust.

Yes, father! Your paired hands
do deftly demonstrate
with the rigor of a lab experiment,
point and counterpoint,
the consummation of a symphony,
that commerce surely does exist
betwixt the test tube and the violin.

Robert Crist
from "Test Tubes & Violins"
- for my father Ray Crist
April, 13,1996

INDUSTRIAL RESEARCH
South Charleston, West Virginia, 1946-1959

At the beginning of 1946, the shutting down of the

Columbia Group, Manhattan District Project, was anticipated, and I decided to move on to another phase in my career. Thus, I was faced with a decision: would I join my colleagues at the University of Chicago, return to Columbia advanced to the rank of full professor, or go to the Union Carbide and Carbon Chemicals Company in Charleston, West Virginia. There my associate from Oak Ridge, George Felbeck, was setting up a research-production project. I would be associated with that project and would also be in charge of the research laboratory at the South Charleston plant.

Work at Carbide represented both change and continuity in my career, since I would be involved in directing research, but now in an industrial setting. During the final year of the Manhattan Project, as director I strove, as I said, to maximize the co-operative productivity of the scientific staff. At times the project's scientists had become involved in conflict and mutual antagonism. This had also been true of the Chemistry faculty at Columbia, where Urey had exerted great pressure for change, and various factions existed. To enhance scientific interaction in the Columbia Group of the Manhattan District Project, I had a meeting with each section head every Monday morning in which I encouraged discussion and mutual engagement in problems. I found that these meetings indeed proved effective, so I followed a similar practice in my work with Carbide both at this time in South Charleston and later in Tarrytown.

A number of factors went into the decision to go to West Virginia. I was seeking a variation in activities—something new to stimulate my interests. At the same time, the element of research remained present, as it would in all phases of my career. Also, Dorothy and I were not inclined to stay in the same metropolitan area or go to another. We believed that bringing up the boys in a small town environment would be advantageous. After all, we had grown up in the Pennsylvania countryside.

Our house in South Charleston was on Massey Circle. This street, ringing the top of a wooded hill, offered a panoramic view of Kanawha Valley, called the 'Magic Valley' because it was lined with highly productive and innovative chemical plants—Union Carbide, Monsanto, DuPont, Westvaco. At that time, environmental awareness was almost nil. The Kanawha River (since cleaned up) was highly polluted, and chemical fumes often filled the air, mainly in the town below, but occasionally to a lesser degree all the way up to Massey Circle. In those days the citizens of the town (who were massively employed by the chemical plants and supporting businesses) tolerated the nasty smells; "It's the odor of money," they said with a smile and a shrug.

On arriving at our new home in June, 1946, I got to work on some useful improvements of the property. Wood paneling made a portion of the basement into a recreation room for the children. A glassed-in porch, an addition to the house, provided a sunny sitting area on the ground level. A heavier project was the new garage. The former garage had been located in the basement of the house, which meant that the car climbed a long, steep driveway—a tricky maneuver which could even be dangerous in winter time. I designed a reinforced concrete garage dug into the hillside just off the street. I built the forms and found steel reinforcement material at various places around town. Carried by wheelbarrow on a ramp across the lawn, the ground from excavation for the garage became fill for the former driveway. I recall the amazement of my neighbors when they found an 'industrial executive' building heavy forms for reinforced concrete, lifting them into place, hoisting massive I-beams for the roof with a block-and-tackle, and pushing heavy loads of dirt in a wheelbarrow on a ramp across the steep lawn. Little could they realize what a joy strenuous physical work always was for me! I also always found that all sorts of tasks around the house were useful introductions to the boys about the practical workings of the world. I tried gardening, too, in South Charleston. While our flower-beds flourished, the clay soil did not support my attempt to grow tomatoes and a few stalks of corn.

How the years flew by! It wasn't long before our 'little boys' were young fellows involved in their various projects and interests. Lance, an accomplished student, was fascinated by machines—disassembling the lawn mower motor and constructing a go-cart powered by that motor. The twins were good at sports. They were strong at tennis,

and I recall the excitement of Henry (at college) bowling 9 strikes in a row. In Boy Scout activities, particularly camping, he was a perfectionist. He was thorough and precise in everything he pursued, but dyslexia was a great burden he had to cope with from his grammar school through his college years. At the time Henry was in school, few educators had heard of dyslexia. We too hadn't heard of it and had no idea that there might be a type of special training that would be helpful for Henry's problem. His teachers only knew that he was a slow reader and reversed letters in reading. He faced the problem basically on his own over years of unceasing and patient effort. His total breakthrough came with outstanding performance in medical school and the pathologist's profession. Showing that overcoming adversity can contribute to character and creativity, his response to challenge contributed to the development of exceptional inherent conceptual abilities. These abilities both enriched his professional achievement and led, for example, to his appointment to the Board of Directors of a major computer company on the basis of his creative ways of approaching problems.

The twins created excellent science projects which they took to local and state academic fairs. Using a vacuum cleaner as his basic mechanism, Lance created a wind-tunnel for testing flow patterns. Henry set up a microscope with a camera to photograph cells. I was always delighted by their fervent devotion and inventiveness in their projects. From boyhood,

they envisioned their respective future professions in science and medicine. Robert's main interests were music and literature. He enjoyed writing essays and poetry, played lead trombone in the high school concert band and in a dance band, sang solo in the church choir, and took the tenor lead in *H.M.S. Pinafore*.

During their high school years, I enjoyed not only

helping as much as I could in support of my sons' academic projects, but also providing them the opportunity to visit my own place of work. I remember one occasion, for example, when Robert came with me into the South Charleston research laboratory and I did bit of glass-blowing to suggest some basics in constructing an apparatus. Years later, when he was in graduate school, he recalled the lab visit, telling me: "You know, Dad, going into your laboratory meant a lot to me. It reminded me of being in Harriet Boyd's studio at the time Henry, Lance, and I sat for that portrait in 1946. It was a very large studio with separate spacious rooms where three painters were at work: Mrs. Boyd, her husband, and their son. That was, at the age of nine, my first contact with creative processes unfolding. Looking back on it now, I think I had the sensation that entering the studio I was experiencing not only a physical space but a region of the artists' minds. Being with you in your laboratory and watching you work was like that—it was your mind that I was visiting."

In the West Virginia period, a humorous event occurred at our church, Christ Church Methodist in Charleston. Rarely do I permit myself to get caught up in 'frivolous' activities, but when a pie-eating contest—of all things!—was held during a party in the church social hall, I somehow let myself be roped into participating. I was to compete with two other men in the speedy devouring of lemon meringue pies. I decided to approach pie-eating scientifically: first I would 'inhale' the meringue; then I would, in a swift circular motion, gobble the filling and crust. The method paid off: I won hands down. However, this was not the end of the incident. The master of ceremonies stepped forward carrying the victor's award: a baby pig. The lively piglet, however, escaped his grasp and scrambled around the room. None of the city churchgoers could latch onto the animal. Fortunately, my farm boy's experience facilitated swift, sure capture of the critter. I built a small enclosure for 'Susie' in our back yard. On one occasion, however, she escaped and paid our neighbors a visit. I will never forget our friend Marge Pace, two houses over, calling us on the phone and demanding with humorous urgency that we instantly retrieve our 'pink pet'. As I recall, we ended up giving piggy to 'Slim Jim' Eccles, one of the workers who was helping us on the excavation for the new garage.

Dorothy's gentleness and caring were the center of our family life. Her nurturing of the children led them into a world of harmony and beauty. She not only appreciated fine music but was herself an excellent violinist. She was the ideal wife and mother, selflessly devoting herself to both the practical tasks of housekeeping and the community relationships which enriched our life in social activities and artistic events. It was through Dorothy that the boys were surrounded with books and records, were introduced to theater and opera, and were endued with spiritual values. It was Dorothy who found Robert an excellent voice teacher, Mrs. Coney, who introduced him to art songs in several languages. I also recall a deeply moving recital which Robert and I attended with Dorothy. The renowned tenor, Roland Hayes, was giving a recital on the campus of a college outside Charleston. The beauty of Hayes's voice was received reverently by the hushed audience. That was an experience which only Dorothy could have offered us. Quiet and self-abnegating—never petty or egotistic, Dorothy was the heart of our family and of my personal life.

In bringing up our sons, Dorothy and I believed, of course, in endowing them with a sense of responsibility and self-discipline. Naturally, I would never use physical punishment to discipline my sons or 'teach them a lesson'. No serious occasions for discipline arose. I remember a minor incident that occurred one time at the dinner table. Dorothy had served a mushroom sauce with the meat and Henry—always a picky eater—complained 'What is this junk!'. I sent him to his room saying that his mother worked very hard to provide for them and I never wanted to near another word of complaint. On another occasion during the junior high school years, one of the twins smacked the other too hard in a childish 'skirmish' and I 'corrected' the guilty party with a couple of light whacks of a ruler on his behind. A comic episode is my sole recollection of letting temper get the best of me. Henry and Lance were costumed as knights for a school play, and I was photographing them. I had all my lights just right, and it was important for them to hold a pose so that the picture could be done properly. However, they began jostling, giggling, and teasing each other. As soon as I got them to settle down, they would irrepressibly start up again. I was so peeved that I dubbed them both with a slight tap from Lance's wooden sword.

Golf is the only game I've ever enjoyed, and my sons and I played golf together during their high school years. The physical exercise among the beautiful hills of the golf course was more important than getting the ball in the cup, and I did the back nine after the course was almost empty, cutting across fairways to avoid other golfers and taking a lot of 'gimmes'. As for card games, I played only bridge, which Dorothy especially enjoyed both for the sake of the company and the interest of playing out the hands. I can't say that I ever could have played a game regularly just for fun, so I poke fun at Robert and his wife Despina, for example, for enthusiastically going at it in backgammon twice every day! I guess I always preferred to combine 'play' with 'work' in the laboratory or chores around the house. As for games as the boys grew up, aside from golf and swimming, the only thing I can recall was a game of 'Rook' at Wattoga State Park in West Virginia, when we also enjoyed pulling taffy. I should mention, too, that we made it a fun occasion to whip up batches of home-made ice-cream on our family visits to my parents' farm.

Literature played a role in our family life. Since

Dorothy had done graduate study in literature, her knowledge of the field was vast in comparison to mine, so she was 'in charge' of the children's going to the theater or attending other literary events. Still, the love of verse had stayed with me since my college days, and in South Charleston, I enjoyed reading poetry to the three boys after Sunday dinner. Following our scrumptious meal—Dorothy was a marvelous cook!—I would recite lyrics by Wordsworth, Tennyson, and Burns, as well as comic verse by Lewis Carroll (who, I later learned, suffered—as I did for a time in later life—from optical migraine). One of my favorite works was Burns's *To a Mouse*, which pleased me because of the farm setting, where the poet plows up a mouse's nest and then apologizes to the 'wee beastie' for 'man's dominion' disrupting nature's 'social union'.

One of our most pleasant, memorable family activities was summer vacations at the farm and the seashore. We would put our English Setter, Happy (his life from puppyhood to old age coincided with the period in Charleston) in a kennel and take off in the always enjoyable and rambunctious car trip to our vacation spots. My parents had moved from the large farm where I grew up to a small farm where they had a few animals and modest plots for raising corn and a few additional vegetables. On our yearly visits to the farm, the children were delighted with contact with the animals—watching my father do the plowing, feeding the hogs (now only four or five), enjoying my mother's 'farm cooking', playing about the fields, and sitting on our old (now rusty) threshing machine which the boys called the 'broom-broom'. Our relatives, Miriam and Doug Beidel, lived in southern New Jersey where Miriam taught high school and Doug was superintendent of schools. Thus, our second vacation spot was Cape May Court House. We stayed at their home, and we were joined there by Dorothy's brother Nick and his family—his charming wife Alice, and their two boys, Mark and Ross. Nick was a forester, and later executive, with West Virginia Pulp and Paper Company in Charleston, South Carolina. Like his father, he was a great story-teller. Mark was around four years older than our boys, while Ross was their age. I think that our boys considered Mark a role model, since he was a fine musician, athlete, and student. (He went on to the Naval Academy, served on nuclear powered submarines, and eventually became an engineer, initially building and finally shutting down nuclear power plants.) I associate both of our family vacation spots with the feeling of the sun—Dorothy, the boys, and I being together by the sea or on the farm in moments so filled with happiness, they seemed timeless.

I recall an amusing incident in communication between Dorothy and me at the time that we had just arrived in Charleston. We were honorary guests at a Rotary dinner, and after dessert we were waiting for some time for the speaker, John Dunning from Columbia, to arrive. Concluding that he had been prevented from coming, the Rotary president asked me to fill in with a few remarks on subject of the evening. With relish I stepped to the podium and spoke for forty minutes on interesting non-classified aspects of our work on the Manhattan Project. As the audience clapped appreciatively and I once more took my seat by Dorothy, I observed that she had an almost astonished look on her face. It seemed that she could hardly prevent her mouth from dropping open. Leaning discreetly toward me, she whispered with awe in my ear, "Why Ray, I never knew how smart you are! How could you manage such a marvelous talk on the spur of the moment! Ray, you're truly amazing!"

My professional life in South Charleston was extremely absorbing and challenging. Our project at the Carbide plant was aimed at producing basic products from coal hydrogenation and gasification. These processes would yield valuable products for use by the various divisions in the Union Carbide Corporation: aliphatics for the

Chemicals Company, carbon for National Carbon, gaseous products for Linde, and starting materials for the Plastics Company. Carbide was a pioneer in the plastics field, as everyone knows from their products like household plastic containers and food wraps. Working in this industrial environment where my researchers were pursuing the phenomenon of polymerization to make these plastics, I was struck by another example of the circles in my experience: I had worked in a lab with Bodenstein who discovered the chain reaction for atoms with molecules, and on the Manhattan Project where the chain reaction involved neutrons with nuclei. Now, at Carbide, it was another chain reaction, this time concerning radicals with monomers that produced polymers.

The coal hydrogenation process had been under investigation for a number of years since its use to make gasoline from coal as heavily subsidized by the wartime German government. Our coal hydrogenation pilot plant was set up on a semi-commercial scale of processing 200 tons of coal daily. During the last three years of its operation, I had responsibility for handling the operation. We reached the point of building a 1,000 ton per day coal plant, but the price of oil kept going down, so we were forced to abandon the venture. In our case, there would be no subsidy to shore up the project.

The coal gasification operation was set up near Charleston in an area rich in coal. At first a 2-3 foot wide hole was dug one hundred feet and fired at the end to start formation of carbon monoxide and hydrogen. This process was pursued for months, with inadequate gas production because of overhead water leakage into the burning area. Finally, this effort was abandoned and Carbide engineers turned their attention to a side interest—the process of digging coal horizontally. They devised a machine 4ft. x 8ft. in front with four cutting wheels and a conveyor belt to remove the coal. This 'coal mole' drove into the seam pouring out coal at a cost of around twenty-five cents per ton. Though Carbide finally did not exploit the coal mole, the company rented it to a major American mining company. Ultimately that company found cheaper means to facilitate their operation. I went to Germany with a colleague to see if any concerns there might be interested in the 'mole'. An initial contact in the Ruhr was not successful, so we were sent to Berlin, where we showed a film of the 'mole' in operation to an audience of highly placed industrialists and businessmen. I narrated as the film demonstrated the machine pouring out coal at such a great rate that two men with shovels were unable to clear it away at the end of the conveyor belt. One of the members of the audience shouted, "This is the first time I've seen Americans work!" German firms were not interested in the machine, but we had a means of obtaining cheap coal, though without an application for our company.

One of my major community interests was in secondary education. On arriving in Charleston, many of our incoming employees were concerned with educational standards. I was committed to raising the level of the local school budget, so I organized a committee which launched a bond issue to raise needed funds. Another activity was membership in the Advisory Board working to revise the state Constitution. The Board arrived at numerous points of revision but in the end these efforts came to nothing, and I had the impression that, unknown to us, the whole affair may have been some sort of political 'showcase'. In regard to my involvement in school interests, an effort which did prove worthwhile was interviewing candidates for the school board. My endorsements were well received, and this was a boon for the more effective operation of the educational system.

The year 1959-60 saw Lance and Henry finishing

their freshman year at college (Swarthmore and Dickinson, respectively). Following graduation from Haverford and Master's work at the University of Chicago, Robert was teaching for a year at Penn State prior to returning to Chicago for doctoral studies. Dorothy and I were also on the move—from South Charleston to Saddle River, New Jersey, since I was shifting my professional base to the Union Carbide Research Institute at Tarrytown, New York. Remembering the connection to Washington Irving's 'Sleepy Hollow', we were returning to familiar territory as we went forward into another phase of endeavor.

Considering the creative thinking of scientists and major advances in science and technology, one must reach deep into the human mind and spirit. . . . In our attempts to create new vision, . . . logic is often insufficient. Here, to fill in the knowledge gaps, there is need for creative human conception, based on our 'subconscious' self. With contemplation, meditation—and patience—our subconscious grows in creative strength, and it becomes capable of making new concepts 'instantaneously' emerge into our thinking mind.

Jule Rabo, Letter to Ray H. Crist
November 15, 2004

UNION CARBIDE RESEARCH INSTITUTE
Tarrytown, New York, 1959-1963

In 1959, on one of my regular trips to New York City to consult with George Felbeck, he informed me that a group at the Manhattan office had a matter to discuss with me. This was the directorship of the Corporation's Research Institute, whose new laboratory was presently under construction at Tarrytown, New York.

Operating at that time at Sterling Forest, New York, the research program mainly involved a Navy-funded investigation of hardness vs. brittleness of projectile outlet tubes at around 2,800 C. On the opening of the new research facility at Tarrytown, I was anxious to find additional projects related to the production of each of

Union Carbide's divisions. To this end, I regularly consulted with chemists in each of the divisions. A key event was meeting chemist Jule Rabo and discovering his dynamic research creativity. Rabo had come to the United States from Hungary, where he had done research on motor fuel. He had come to work in our Linde division. He discussed his ideas about research with me, and his insights led to my enthusiastic invitation to him to come to the institute. He proceeded to do remarkably productive work on petroleum-related products. His creativity and fruitful cooperation with the various Carbide groups represented my ideal conception of a research institute scientist. The outstanding feature of his approach was that of individual thinking and initiative geared toward practical applications. Thus, he illustrated the phenomenon that I observed throughout my career—namely that creativity comes about through a combination of imaginative individual initiative and fortuitous circumstances. The director cannot manage research so as to bring about novel discoveries; he can only provide a framework to stimulate dynamic inventiveness. In mid-November, 2004, I was gratified to receive a letter from Jule confirming that as director at the Institute I had been successful in providing an environment in which individual creativity could flourish. "You had great expectations from us [researchers]," he writes, "but we never felt pressure; your guidance was kept on the basis of feeling the deep human spirit. . . . I felt always energized and inspired. You found the right way to 'manage' a creative research organization. . . . These thoughts strongly support your management style [which concentrates] on strengthening the basic, human creative spirit."

The object of research is to generate creative, novel ideas. But this goal is difficult to achieve in a profit-oriented industrial setting. Union Carbide began in mid-century with President George Curme seeking novel processes to produce aliphatic chemicals from ethylene. His success made the company the number one producer of aliphatics. To stimulate novel discoveries, in 1947 Curme set up a research institute in Brussels staffed by German research scientists. This institute was in operation around eight years but made no substantial contribution to the corporation. Again, in the fifties, he released two men from production work in each of the five Carbide divisions to work on basic research. After five years, no striking results occurred. This shows that novelty cannot be managed. On the other hand, spontaneous individual inventiveness is dramatic, as in the case of Jule Rabo, cited above, and of my associates Hugh Davis, Tom Wilson, and George O' Connor, in Charleston who—working entirely on their own initiative on ethylene production, polymerization, and organic synthesis—made remarkable and highly profitable discoveries. In short, my experience both in academia and in industry, from Columbia, to the Manhattan Project, to Carbide research institutes, was that the discovery of novelty cannot be programmed and directed. It arises by individual initiative, creativity, and devotion to group goals—together, of course, with an element of luck.

Serendipity—a fortunate productive combination of circumstances—is an element that has played a significant role in scientific discovery just as it has in all creative fields. I noted above that on the Manhattan Project it was—of all things—part of a paint sprayer, the invention of an interior decorator, Ed Norris, that solved one of the thorny problems we encountered. Norris turned up at the Project almost like a *deus ex machina*! In another case, curiosity led to a chance discovery. A Dupont scientist was puzzled because a tank which was supposed to contain a gas appeared empty. Cutting open the tank, he found that its walls were covered with a waxy white substance which proved to be resistant to corrosive reagents. The substance, eventually named Teflon, was used for gasket material in the UF_6 gaseous diffusion plant of the Manhattan Project before it was introduced into

American kitchens (Roberts 1989: 187-188). A much earlier example was a historic land-mark in chemistry. The discovery of the main property of oxygen was influenced by a chance event. At a crucial stage in his experiments, Joseph Priestly—who came to live in central Pennsylvania and some of whose scientific equipment ended up at Dickinson College—confirmed the presence and qualities of the gas which came to be called oxygen by an impulsive test with a burning candle which happened to be standing by. "If I had not had, for some other purpose, to have a lighted candle before me," Priestly said, "I should probably never have made the trial" (Roberts: 27).

So, discovery blossoms through strange combinations of curiosity, intuition, and chance events. It is evident, in turn, that technological success has had unintended mixed results. The disappearance of the work horse led to over-consumption of fossil fuels, useful chemicals brought the side-effect of environmental pollution, nuclear power resulted in a dangerous threat both to human life and the natural environment. In our present fossil fuels crisis and era of nuclear arms proliferation, we can only hope that inventive ingenuity and the spirit of human brotherhood may help evade global catastrophe.

Work at the Institute was a challenge I was eager to accept. My aim as director was to encourage the researchers' concentration on productive inventiveness and cooperation between all the divisions of the company. Both my predecessor and my successor believed in management and somewhat slighted the encouragement of creative individuality, and for this reason the institute did not flourish during those periods. Another incident illustrates my approach to laboratory activity. The Carbide main office sent me a number of lauded works of contemporary painting which they wanted to hang in the institute lobby. They asked me to participate in the process of selection. The works, which were large, flamboyant abstract paintings by outstanding contemporary artists, were brought to the

lobby and hung for our consideration. In the end, I decided that we should not have these or any paintings hanging in the entrance to our building. One consideration was that I could not arrive at a consensus among the researchers as to which of the particular works were indeed attractive as art or possessed some sort of thematic affinity to our purposes. A more important consideration for me, however, was my conviction that making a 'gallery' or 'museum' out of our lobby was not in accord with the objectives of a research laboratory, which should concentrate on theoretical and applied scientific concerns. A feature of our focus on the creative process in science was seminars featuring outstanding scientists from around the country, for example, George Hammett from Cal Tech , a pioneer in organic photochemistry. And then there was the presence of Louis Hammond one year. He had just stepped down as chairman of the Chemistry Department at Columbia, and I invited him to spend the year with us fulltime. "But what will I do?" he asked. "Just walk around and talk with people." He did that very productively.

One of the most wonderful family experiences during this period at Saddle River was Henry's acceptance at medical school. From the time of his childhood, as I mentioned, reading challenges made schoolwork extraordinarily taxing for him. Consequently, he was always finding ways to improve his performance, and Dorothy and I, of course, gave him all the help we could. He would, moreover, always go to summer school to prepare for courses that were particularly demanding or to make up for courses in which he had been weak. At this time in Saddle

River, he was in his senior year at Dickinson. He had worked painfully, arduously—even heroically—to get through the pre-med program, but between him and his dream was the immense hurdle of admission to medical school. One week-day, when I was as usual at work in Tarrytown, a letter addressed to him arrived at Saddle River. It was from the Admissions Office, University of Maryland Medical School. With his heart in his mouth, Henry opened the letter, and he found—that he was accepted! In his joy, having shared the wonderful news with Dorothy, he decided to let me learn of the event in an unorthodox way. Carefully resealing the letter, in conspiracy with his mother, he slipped it into a pile of correspondence addressed to me—bills, notices, and the like. That evening, sitting on the couch and sifting through the mail, I came upon the letter, and without looking at the name of the addressee on the envelope, I casually opened it. It seems I was a bit absent-minded, for I unsuspectingly began to scan the letter without fathoming the context or to whom it was addressed. As my eye went down the lines, I was baffled—what on earth was this letter about? Finally, carefully focusing on the concluding acceptance and letterhead, I was overjoyed with Henry's victory. I leaped up from the couch and impulsively threw my arm around my son's shoulders. I was deeply touched. He had worked so agonizingly and faithfully to achieve this success. "How wonderful! How magnificent!" I shouted in a rare outburst of emotion. "Thank God! What splendid news! Why, you naughty guy, what a beautiful trick to play on your old man!"

A lot was happening in our family life during the 1960's. Robert and Lance were pursuing doctoral work in literature and chemistry, respectively, and Henry was in medical school. All three had begun their own family life; and, in 1961, our first grandchild was born. Eventually there would be nine grandchildren and, to date, fifteen great-grandchildren. Living in the Eastern United States, in

Chicago, in western Virginia, and in Greece, the

grandchildren, now at the height of their careers, are engaged in a variety of callings—homemaking, computer science, finance, elementary school teaching, dance and theater, early education intervention, social work, nursing, photography, and higher education. As it turned out, this was the time when there was also a change in my own professional endeavors, since I returned to higher education as a volunteer educator in 1963.

'Tis not too late to seek a newer world.
Push off, and sitting well in order smite
The sounding furrows; for my purpose holds
To sail beyond the sunset, and the baths
Of all the Western stars, until I die.
It may be that the gulfs will wash us down;
It may be we shall touch the Happy Isles,
And see the great Achilles, whom we knew.
Tho' much is taken, much abides, and tho'
We are not now that strength which in old days
Moved earth and heaven, that which now we are,
One equal temper of heroic hearts,
Made weak by time and fate, but strong in will
To strive, to seek, to find, and not to yield.

Alfred Tennyson
from "Ulysses"

DICKINSON COLLEGE—THE HISTORY OF SCIENCE
Carlisle, Pennsylvania, 1963-1970

The change in my life was precipitated by a profound shock. In June, 1963, I was plunged into darkness when my beloved partner in life was struck by a fatal heart attack. Since the fifties, Dorothy had suffered with heart problems, which forced her to avoid strenuous activity. In Charleston, I moved our bedroom to the first floor, and we also lived on one floor in Saddle River. That devastating summer night Dorothy complained of severe chest pains, and I phoned for an ambulance. As I held her hand waiting for help, her eyes closed, and with indescribable anguish I realized that she was gone. From that instant forward, I have been unable to face the scene, and a sense of her loss is with me from moment to moment. When my time comes, as nature determines, I pray that I will be worthy of being laid to rest by her side.

The devastation that I was undergoing led me to scrutinize my future commitments. I found it unbearable to go on in the place where Dorothy and I had spent the last several years. Examining the course of developments in science through the course of history—and particularly the impact of the recent surge in technology—I became inspired by the idea of undertaking a personal scientific and social mission: helping today's college students, non-science majors in particular, understand the impact of science and technology on history and the environment. After all, they would become the social and political leaders of the future. Thus, I decided to leave my research work with Union Carbide and on a voluntary basis join the Chemistry faculty of Dickinson College. Once more, then, I found my way forward at the same time I was circling back to an earlier setting in my life. The farm boy was returning to rural (now also suburban) Pennsylvania!

Prior to the move to Carlisle—where I rediscovered the scenes of my childhood and youth—Henry and I took a western tour to the Grand Canyon, Yellowstone Park, and Yosemite Park. This time of sharing contributed profoundly to the healing process which at first seemed to me out of reach. Bonding with my sons has always been central to my life, and in this case Henry's quiet companionship and deft handling of our trip meant so much, as I found my way, somehow, into a new phase of experience. The vastness, variety and beauty of the natural settings also played no small part of the regenerating effect of that unforgettable journey. Viewing the wonders of scenery and wildlife in the West, I felt more than ever the import of the song *America*, which hymns the panorama of the American countryside in relation to the national character. The power and grandeur of the natural world contributed, moreover, to launching my mission relating to the creative role of science and culture in the renewal of the environment.

Arriving at Carlisle, I had a small home built for me at 619 Devonshire Drive. The lot for the house was part of a former farm. Before the structure was completed, the rat-infested farm shed adjacent to my lot was torn down, and

there were still the remains of a cement watering-trough in my back yard! So, at Dickinson College, I began my mission in a fresh personal setting which, at the same time, recalled my boyhood origins. Excited by my new commitment, I turned my mind to the impact of science on society throughout the modern era. As I have noted, each phase of my career had brought me to a sense of widening human threat to the environment. I became concerned with environmental pollution in 1941-1945 with the Manhattan Project—involving nuclear energy and possible disastrous environmental contamination—and in 1946-1959, working with the chemical industry in Charleston, West Virginia, where the air was polluted and the Kanawha River was contaminated with chemical wastes. All of these concerns were interrelated with the general impact of science and technology on the world. At Dickinson College between 1963 and 1970, with the valuable support of colleagues like Howard Long, I taught a course in Freshman Chemistry two days per week, and on the third day I stressed themes central to my mission, discussing science's implications in society and industry where it introduced radical changes. Furthermore, my course in the History of Science—along with courses in other areas such as literature, philosophy, and religion—helped provide students with a valuable perspective on the dynamics of the human spirit. My course emphasized the widespread impact of technological innovations on human history and culture—for example, the invention of the stirrup, the introduction of horses for plowing, the use of iron for weaponry, and the like, up to the modern era of nuclear power. In this course the students' main project was an extensive research paper on an issue in science and technology that was of personal interest. Working closely with each student throughout the semester, I found that their interest, research, and writing were very strong. Most of the papers produced were truly outstanding.

One of my most pleasurable leisure-time activities during these years was getting out on the golf course. I played with colleagues from Dickinson on weekends, but I especially liked going out on my own week-day evenings. I had played golf, of course, in Charleston, but now as I was alone in my sixties being on the golf course was something special for me. Beyond the exercise, there was the precious experience of just going along with the feeling of the ground under my feet, the smell of the grass on the fairway—letting my eye be carried off into the sweep of the sky, softly marked by the swirl of clouds. That peaceful yet powerful feeling of being at one with nature in her breadth and wonder was what I found again and again as I returned to the fairways.

Living in Carlisle, each day I was moving to and fro, then, within the area where I grew up and my life took its initial directions. Over the years, as I drove past the old farm home near Lisburn Road, I saw the shed and barn torn down, the house now surrounded and its fields occupied by a suburban neighborhood. Thank God, the house remains standing to this day! A melancholy sight was the spot where the schoolhouse stood that was Dorothy's first place of teaching. Without her going to teach at Shepherdstown, we never would have met. What a blessed event for us! Now the past is memory, and there is bare, raw ground where the building stood.

Teaching duties at Dickinson, and later at Messiah College, required that I organize my life in such a way as to facilitate my work. In preparation for meals, I had a regular menu, and did all my cooking for evening meals on Sunday—putting servings of meat, vegetables, and broth into separate packages which were then frozen, to be brought out and quickly prepared each evening when I returned from my laboratory. I found that regulation of my diet was highly beneficial. For example, daily servings of stewed apples not only kept my digestive system regular but helped forestall optical migraine, which I experienced from time to time. Throughout my life I tried to treat my body and diet in such a way as both to solve problems which arose and to enhance my health. For a period at Columbia, for example, I tried to treat a back condition by sleeping on a board. In Carlisle in the seventies, I experimented with the daily amounts of salt I consumed, systematically increasing and decreasing the amounts so as to monitor the effect.

Nothing pleased me more in the long Pennsylvania nights alone than the comfort of a fire in my living room hearth, with its swirling colors, warmth, and crackling sounds. No longer did I cut the firewood myself, but I bought it instead from a man canvassing the neighborhood for possible sales. His wood wasn't of high quality, but I wanted him to benefit from my purchase, as I knew he was striving to maintain his independence and get along in life. I guess that all along I've respected people for who they are and the work they do, not their prestige. It seemed that at the receptions, for example, I valued time chatting with the custodians as much as contact with distinguished guests with whom I was 'supposed' to converse. Perhaps this attitude relates to my worldview about the nature of living things. There's no such thing as an 'insignificant' or 'uninteresting' atom!

During these years, I did virtually all my shopping at the Farmer's Market in Carlisle on York Pike, which was open on Fridays and Saturdays. I always enjoyed visiting the Market, for it brought back strong associations from my childhood years. Unfortunately, there were now relatively few practicing farmers selling their produce, since the family farm producing a variety of vegetables and fruit had largely been replaced by large single-product business organizations.

At this time, many developments were unfolding in our family life. Lance was on the Chemistry faculty at Georgetown University. After specialty training at Johns Hopkins, Henry was a pathologist at St. Joseph's Hospital in Baltimore. Robert was teaching at the American College of Greece and eventually would join the faculty of the University of Athens. In 1968, I had an opportunity to visit Greece. My stay began in the Athens neighborhood of Hymittos, where Despina grew up. I met Despina's parents and learned that they had been refugees from Asia Minor who had been driven from Turkey in the 1920's by violent political oppression. Hearing that, I recalled that when I attended Messiah School I had Kurdish classmates who had also fled from Turkey to save their lives. Many years after my visit to her neighborhood of Hymittos, Despina wrote a novel *Nostos* (2001) which showed her parents' families in Asia Minor before their expulsion from Turkey and afterwards in Athens. I was interested also to find that the novel introduced the friendship that had developed in Chicago of the '60's between Despina and Laura Fermi, the gifted, gracious widow of my great Manhattan Project colleague.

During the visit to Greece, my long-time interest in ancient history and culture was rewarded by trips to archaeological sites throughout Greece. Despina, Robert and I went to Delphi, Corinth, Olympia, and Crete, where Minos's palace at Knossos offered colorful insights concerning the way of life in Minoan culture. In relation to Crete, I was able to visit Professor Galanopoulos of the University of Athens. I had read a fascinating article of his, probably in *Scientific American.* Its theme was the destruction of Minoan civilization by the tidal wave from the eruption of the volcano at Santorini. The volcano's obliteration of Santorini itself at the height of its development also suggested that island's possible identification with the lost Atlantis.

Life in Carlisle was enriched with visits by my sons' families. As they converged on Devonshire Drive, I enjoyed watching the children play and snapping pictures. The developing of black and white pictures and working up of prints were an old hobby of mine. For example, over the years I attempted to capture images of landscapes and other settings that are symbolically evocative in various ways. I found cascading waterfalls, tangled bare tree limbs against a background of snow, the skeletal remains of a barn, and bleak railroad tracks to be powerful symbols of the course of human life. I hope, too, that I was also able to record some vivid moments in our family experience—the children frolicking in my back yard, a child listening intently to a story, or following with fascination the movement of a caterpillar or turtle. One application of my photography hobby was Christmas cards—black and white prints of a landscape or family scene pasted on a piece of red cardboard.

The professional setting of my activity changed in 1970, for teaching at Dickinson came to an end because of the rule of mandatory retirement at the college. I was troubled by the thought that the continuity of my educational mission was threatened. Where could I now renew my commitment?

RAY H. CRIST

We must trust the perfection of creation so far as to believe that whatever curiosity the order of things has awakened in our minds, the order of things can satisfy. Every man's condition is a solution in hieroglyphic to those inquiries he would put. He acts life, before he apprehends it as truth. . .

Ralph Waldo Emerson
from *Nature*

MESSIAH COLLEGE— RESEARCH IN ENVIRONMENTAL CHEMISTRY
Grantham, Pennsylvania, 1971-2004

A cue to the next facet of my quest came when I visited Messiah College—my old and first alma mater—to give a talk on science in today's world. The enthusiastic reception of my presentation by a packed amphitheater led me to approach the science faculty in search of a place to continue my voluntary contribution to education.

Circling back, then, even more deeply into my roots, I began teaching at Messiah College with a series of lectures to freshmen regarding science and its social consequences. In an Ecology course, I emphasized environmental problems. I had students experiment with drainage of toxic metals down a hill and with lead paint, which causes mental deficiency in children (recall the effect of lead water piping on Roman aristocrats). We also worked with ammonia-derived chemicals as a fertilizer which on going to nitrate in the soil form nitrous oxide. This gas goes into the upper atmosphere where after years in increasing concentration it tends to decompose ozone, which normally keeps ultraviolet radiation from overheating the atmosphere. As I worked in my laboratory, students joined me to learn about my research and discuss other matters in a one-to-one situation.

My involvement in the area of Ecology sparked interest on the part of the Messiah science faculty, so that courses were added and eventually a full-fledged Environmental Studies Program was established.

Now at the age of seventy, my curiosity toward how nature works was leading me into a new productive area of research. I had occasion at home to grow a Christmas lily. Looking at its thick roots made me wonder how metal ions moved from soil into plants. I immersed the roots in water with lead, finding the metal was quickly taken up. With chairman Kenneth Hoover, we thought that algae would be a good living material to study. Thus began my new major activity from the age of seventy-four to one hundred four—that is, working with the ion exchange process of toxic metals in relation to various biological materials.

Over the years surface chemistry was considered a process in which residual surface charges attracted and held free moving gases or ions, known as an adsorptive process. In my work with the alga *Vaucheria*, however, I observed that metal uptake was accompanied by release of a proton from the algae, and for my 1981 paper in *Environmental Science & Technology* I received 150 reprint requests. It is to be noted that plant and animal tissues have a great variety of functional groups that tend to bind with protons. Since this is a labile bonding, I concluded that added metal ions readily exchange with protons or other metals existing at surface sites X. Thus, for example, added Pb^{2+} gives the equilibrium systems:

$$Pb^{2+} + 2HX = 2H^{+} + PbX_2$$

$$Pb^{2+} + CaX_2 = Ca^{2+} + PbX_2$$

In working with various toxic metals and biomaterials, I determined the ion exchange process experimentally, demonstrating that it is a thermodynamic process.

My first experiment was with *Vaucheria*, which was available throughout the year growing in constant temperature spring water. I greatly enjoyed my expeditions to various springs in the Carlisle area where I collected samples for experiments. Visits to pools and brooks into which I would wade to collect my algae specimens enabled me literally to plunge into the natural world, to enter into contact with earth, water, and living things—again and again renewing my delight in affinity with them. *Vaucheria* experiments were followed by experiments with sea water algae obtained from the Smithsonian aquarium. A report of the ion exchange process was presented by Bob Martin at the Engineering Foundation conference in California, 1991. I proceeded to experiments with ion exchange processes in peat moss and fish gills.

The next step was work with lignin, a by-product of paper production which has no direct use. As it turned out, my work showed that lignin is very effective in absorbing toxic metals. Using an organic solvent and binder, I developed a plastic form of lignin. On drying, the solid strips or beads are effective in removing toxic metal contaminants from water. This work was reported by Lance in Scotland, and later in Korea. Furthermore, it seemed that the lignin material was so promising for biosorption that we filed for a patent. Since MeadWestvaco (formerly West Virginia Pulp and Paper) would be the most likely company to license our process, Lance went to their laboratory in Charleston, South Carolina, to try to convince them of its use. So there was Lance, starting his presentation to their Research and Development personnel with the words, "I feel at home here, since I have heard about this place long ago from my Uncle Nick."

During these years in my Messiah College laboratory, both my family and the College kindly hosted celebrations marking key points in my life and my career as a volunteer educator. On April 13, 1996, Messiah College held an award dinner "For 25 Years Modeling Excellence in Scientific Research." Many colleagues and friends from the past and present joined me at the dinner. Prior to the brief award ceremony, Henry and Lance spoke of how I'd inspired them as a father and scientist, my granddaughter Joanna warmly thanked me as a grand-pa who had also influenced her in her life and academic career, and Robert read his poem entitled "Test Tubes & Violins." Other out-of-towners added their appreciative remarks, including my former Columbia student Lou Baker and Union Carbide co-worker Tom Wilson. Another delightful occasion was my centenary birthday celebration in Carlisle, which was attended by many family members, friends, and associates. Once again my heart was warmed by lively comments from those present. My granddaughter, Eileen, contributed by reading Robert's 100-line poem, "Centenary Verses," sent to me from Greece for the occasion.

For my 100th birthday, Lance offered to take me to Charleston, West Virginia, to revisit Carbide and drive around the old neighborhoods. For each reason he had for going, I thought up one for not going. Finally I had to admit my real reason for refusing: it just wouldn't be the same there without Dorothy, and I couldn't stand that. Well, the passage of two more years presented a reason that I could not refute. Former Carbiders apparently saw a four-page article about the different phases of my career in *Chemical & Engineering News*, the trade journal of the American Chemical Society. This led to an invitation from the Kanawha Valley Section of the ACS to attend their Fall Banquet and present an address. To my surprise the keynote speaker who followed my thirty minutes of remarks was Eli Pierce, President of the National ACS. But what memories flooded back as I breakfasted with my Carbide friends, drove around Massey Circle, and looked once more at the reinforced concrete garage I had constructed. Standing in the driveway, I chatted with our next door neighbor Leonard Robb, who told me how delighted he was to see me. He said that over the decades he had always hoped that before he died he would again set eyes on 'Doc Crist'.

My final experiments in my Messiah lab involved the question, probably the most complicated one I asked of nature, how toxic metals were taken up by *living* plants. Our previous work had helped us with the answer to that question for isolated roots, but what about a living plant? Results might prove useful in the relatively new field called phytoremediation, namely the growing of plants in polluted soil to detoxify the soil. A crucial experiment was to put the root systems of living plants in two solutions of metal ions, one with the metal in its normal positive-charged form, the other with the metal complexed in a way that caused it to carry a negative charge. I was astounded to observe that the negative form was carried faster from solution through roots up to leaves—a process different from our ion exchange must be occurring. A natural process was telling me that the negative form was swept up with the water, while the positive forms proceeded with successive ion exchange steps. This was not the first time that nature told me something different from what I expected; thus I was once more reminded, at the end of my research career, how to listen to her secrets. And so at 104, I was able to share this new understanding with the scientific community in a paper that just appeared in the *International Journal of Phytoremediation,* which had honored me with editorial Commentary in 2002 entitled "Phytoremediation's Centenarian — An Interdisciplinary Journey through Science."

Over the course of recent years, my peaceful life as a researcher has been 'interrupted' by award ceremonies, interviews and public appearances. To characterize these honors as 'interruptions', I admit, sounds harsh. I only mean that I would prefer not to be in the limelight, but instead just pursue my work quietly in the sanctum of my laboratory. However, I am grateful for these occasions and must say that as I get into the spirit of things, I can even work up some enthusiasm, for I see these occasions not as a celebration of me, but as a way of emphasizing the importance of the pursuits of science. My major public appearances began in 2000 with the PBS feature, *The Living Century — Ray Crist, A Teacher and Student for Life*. One of the producers of this half-hour TV special was Barbara Streisand. Her co-producers, Chris Carson and Steve Latham, who directed the production superbly, came to know about me through my granddaughter Joanna's

husband, Ben, one of Steve's college friends. The program, which was introduced by Jack Lemon, was a very powerful treatment of all facets of my life. Over the four-year period since, it has been seen by three to four million viewers, and portions of this program and others have been shown on other TV stations both in the United States and abroad (I have been told, for example of news bytes appearing in Vietnam and Greece).

The Living Century opened the flood-gate. I was contacted by telephone for a study of aging conducted by Harvard University. In turn, I was co-featured in a segment about centenarians on the *CBS Sunday Morning* show, narrated by Walter Cronkite. Then came segments on the National Geographic channel, a local TV station, and *60 Minutes*. Furthermore, an interview appeared on CNN, there were many radio interviews from Canada as well as the United States, newspapers covered my story, and there were articles on the internet. I have also been approached for live TV appearances—which I cannot do—by the Jay Leno Show, Dave Letterman, *Today*, and the *CBS Morning Show*. Public appearances have required that I replace my usual casual attire with something else altogether. Imagine me in a tuxedo, which I call a 'monkey suit'! Well, you might be able to do that, but I couldn't. Yet there I was, spruced up in a tux for the Central Pennsylvania Technology Council Awards Banquet where I received their first Lifetime Achievement Award. Apparently the crowd of over 300 liked my remarks on 'You Can't Manage Novelty', since they got on their feet applauding three different times. To make sure they understood who was behind the tux, I launched my talk with, "I'm just a farm boy!"

The 'farm boy' was in

a tux once more going to Washington, D.C., to accept the Experience Works award for America's Outstanding Oldest Worker 2002. Experience Works recognizes older workers who "exemplify the valuable contribution that older individuals are making in their communities and places of work." I had received the Pennsylvania State Award from this organization, and then was given the National award in Washington, D.C. It was five days in the capital for us winners from all the states, filled with events such as visiting our respective congressmen and even a dinner cruise on the Potomac. In my case, there was a special press conference where I accepted the award as national winner, and a congratulatory letter from the ACS was read. Of course I

took the opportunity to express my ideas on novelty. And at the end of the week, a black tie banquet took place in Union Station where I once again spoke about novelty in the award address.

Working over the years in my laboratory, pursuing problems that have come to my mind, and devising effective research methods, I have had experiences which are more gratifying than I can say. For decades, as a research director, I had been facilitating others' investigation of matters that had been dictated by the context in which we were working. Now, in my Messiah laboratory, I was once more on my own, as I had been as an assistant professor at Columbia. How invigorating and rejuvenating it was! As I approached the age of one hundred, I felt as if I were reliving the days of my young manhood! I was also gratified by the relations at Messiah among faculty members as well as between students and faculty. That very spiritual harmony which I discovered at Messiah in 1911 again came into my life almost a century later. My spirit was indeed nurtured by this atmosphere, supporting my work as I moved into my declining years. Stimulated by my environmental experiments, at the same time I was contending with health problems that threatened my ability to push forward in my life and mission. Deteriorating eyesight has meant that I have read and walked with increasing difficulty. Fortunately, a special pair of prism eye-glasses, which I helped design, aided in reading, as well as a screen projecting large-letter texts. In the laboratory I read gauges with my eye up very close. I stopped driving in 1983, and since then a number of individuals at Messiah College—especially Harold Fraker (whom I called my 'picker upper')—have kindly provided me a ride to and from the College, enabling me to work in the laboratory from 8:30 in the morning till 6:00 in the evening.

As regards health, I also experienced crises with cardiac arrhythmia. During the 1980's there were occasions in which I would suddenly pass out. One of these incidents occurred in the bank, and another in church. Both times I was rushed to the hospital emergency room, where I would recover. In the latter case, a comic event took place after I was released from the ER. Since I had found by experimentation that as I conjectured a judicious sip of alcohol would help my circulation, I carried in my coat pocket a small plastic Maalox bottle containing a medicinal dose of whisky. In the emergency room after the church episode, this bottle was found on me, and the attending physician later told his colleague, Henry—without knowing our relationship—that an elderly man who had passed out 'in his cups' at church had been revived in the Carlisle Hospital ER!

For a long time doctors were unable to diagnose the cause of my brief fainting episodes. The detection of arrhythmia was, however, finally achieved and the problem solved following a life-threatening episode that occurred when, luckily, Henry happened to be sitting with me in the living room. As we were casually talking, I suddenly lost consciousness. I was rushed to the hospital where my life was saved and a pace-maker was implanted to regulate the rhythm of my heart. That once more Henry was by my side to preserve and facilitate my life is an event that is stored in

my heart with deep love and gratitude.

To go on living is to go on discovering. My primary

delight has always been to come in direct contact with life processes in their intricate, amazing mechanisms. I like to get my hands on things to get a sense of reality. Whenever I come into contact with something new, I want to hold it in my hands. This is true both in the world in general and in the lab. I delight in designing my own apparatus suited to the problem at hand. For example, on the Manhattan Project I had to invent a new way of measuring pressure. I came up with an unusual apparatus produced by some imaginative glass blowing. Then, years later, to monitor the progress of a column chromatography in a biosorption experiment, I devised a column that had syringe ports along its length to sample the effluent.

As I work in the laboratory, I enjoy 'feeling my way along'—or, perhaps more accurately, sometimes, 'stumbling ahead'. If something doesn't work at first, I seek the right modification. I have to keep on my toes. I realize that Nature is telling me something, so I listen alertly to find the next step, continuing the cycle until I arrive at sound data and publishable results.

Throughout publication of my research, Lance—son and colleague—has worked closely with me as I shape up my lab results for publication. I do the experiments, record the data, and write the first drafts of papers. Lance looks up the relevant literature, helping to arrive at the final version of the paper, just as he does our correspondence with journal editors and referees. I recall one instance when a referee failed to grasp a point, and I commented, "Well, if he doesn't agree, he can just—go stand on his head!" Lance laughed, commenting that it has always been one of my proper 'Victorian' characteristics to avoid violent and unseemly language of any sort. I can only agree that truly I have always eschewed indecorous words, just as I have habitually lamented unmanly deeds. On the other hand, I have deeply enjoyed the humorous use of language, as well as plays on words and an understanding of word derivations.

As for humor, I recall an incident at Columbia when an arresting original idea was generated by a colleague, and I exclaimed, "Why, good for you! I'll bet you a cow that's correct!"

My sharing ideas with Lance and our collaboration on papers have been sources of deep satisfaction for me. He has also reported some of our work at international conferences. A dramatic event in this connection was his presentation of our work on lignin and fish gills at the conference of the International Adsorption Society at Nagasaki, Japan, in 2001. This report at Nagasaki constituted yet another circling of events in my life. Work on the Manhattan Project had been one of the forces leading up to the atomic devastation of beautiful Nagasaki, but now—fifty-five years later—our presentation was bringing to that very city a peaceful message of environmental concern.

In the later decades of my life, as I withdrew from industrial research and returned to my alma maters Dickinson and Messiah in pursuit of my mission, I obviously did not have 'retirement' in mind, but on the contrary, an ongoing cycle of engagement in life and work. Inevitably, however, in spite of my stubborn refusal to acknowledge the concept, a retirement ceremony was fated to take place. What an embarrassing day, then, was April 13, 2004, at Messiah College where this very event began with a TV interview in the lobby before entering the auditorium for the college's annual Recognition Day. After students were recognized for their various scholastic, athletic, and service achievements, the Dean spoke about my years at Messiah and showed film clips of the PBS *Living Century* feature. At his conclusion I felt moved to stand and face the student body, raise both arms in the air, and call out, "God bless you all!" To think that almost a century before I would have been one of the students sitting out there. What a different gathering it would have been.

After three more TV interviews and two newspaper interviews in the now empty auditorium, we went to a reception room for cake and punch and an informal time for Messiah faculty and staff to stand and make comments or approach my chair for a chat. The College arranged for an announcement to be sent out on the AP wire. My long-deferred retirement thus became global knowledge, as my grandchildren informed me, over the internet.

For me the past two decades have been the story of finding ways to cope with my dwindling sight and hearing both for sheer survival and for the sake of the work which I want to accomplish. Uncorrectable macular degeneration caused my sight to become increasingly poor during the 1980's and thereafter. Being dependent on myself for daily transportation to and from Messiah College, I stubbornly stayed behind the wheel long after common sense told me driving was no longer feasible. I was determined to drive that road just as I drove myself ahead with dimming sight in the laboratory. Some close calls on the road, however, showed me that I would have to give up driving. So, my drivers, family or others, aid me in coping with an impediment. In turn, a circle of people have thoughtfully supported me in diverse ways. My sons are trusty jacks of all trades in this respect. Donna Crist has over the years provided a caring woman's touch in so many facets of my day-to-day needs; Despina is always there for me like the daughter I never had, affectionate, vital, and humorous; and Vonny Eckman, bless her, has been of great assistance, skillfully efficient and, above all, warm and comforting.

Through the course of decades of research at

Messiah College, association with all my colleagues was both cordial and essential. Bob Martin and Karl Oberholtzer, in particular, shared my interests, supported my efforts, and provided practical help, aiding me, for example, in coping with my declining eyesight in the laboratory context. Without Bob's keeping instruments running, I wonder what

I could have accomplished.

My last laboratory investigation involving toxic metal uptake by sunflower, switchgrass, and Alyssum also necessitated extensive help. Along with my Messiah colleagues, Bethann Rusenko was truly outstanding in contributing to my work in the laboratory. She kept my experiments in order, worked up the data, and searched the internet for relevant literature.

Support has also contributed to the writing of these memoirs. First I sit in my chair pondering a given thought, episode, or experience, and then go to my desk. Barely seeing the paper, I write down six to eight pages as quickly as I can, without stopping. If I stop, I won't be able to pick up the thread because it's increasingly difficult even to read my own writing. Thank goodness my helpers have become proficient at reading my scrawl and asking the right questions so as to fill in the missing pieces.

In a poem, my son put in words my thanks to each person who has so kindly aided me in my journey:

"There are no words, no thanks to express what you have done
As I so reluctantly end my work,
Fighting with every ounce of myself as I ebb away
To make some final run,
To find some elusive piece,
Yet knowing there is no end
Save that treasure, a crack opening to the next mystery.

"As the ending despite my curse became my final mission,
It has been you who rowed me in grace across the Styx,
Kept me in tow, in balance,
To stay as a foremast.

"As a god, you came to lift the fallen Hero
To hold him high
Till his final Act was done."

Henry Crist

EPILOGUE

THE LAST EXPERIMENT, March 8, 2004

Thus, shortly after my 104th birthday I performed my last experiment. The place was marked by a name-plate saying, LABORATORY: RAY CRIST. To me, my very life has been a laboratory that I have been blessed to work in, to develop, to share with the world. Looking back over a life filled with ongoing challenges and the beauty of discovery, I believe that nature, the cosmos, has blessed man with the ability to blend feeling and thought in such a way that discovery is always multidimensional and unending. As feelings are linked to the mind, as emotions are allowed to have their due with the intellect, new understandings are found and knowledge is advanced.

I think of the divine as the Mystery of the Almighty—the power that is 'unprovable' yet paradoxically ever-present, granting us the privilege to probe unendingly what Keats called the blended truth and beauty of the universe. My passion has been a humble search for that blend of rational, intuitive, and emotional realization. Born one with the earth and with a mind formed in the mold of the scientific process, I have sought a mode of being in which the intellect, the heart, and the earth come together.

My convictions are that nature will guide us in this search for unity, but we must be sensitively attuned to what she is telling us, so that knowledge will come from curiosity, from the freedom and desire to let ideas happen, from the encouragement of novelty. That is a passion we must have—a passion for openness which perhaps can lead us to those innovations that can preserve the earth.

As I closed the door of my laboratory through which I would never walk again, I experienced an intense realization of bringing to an end over a century of rewarding life in science and the community, and passing into the final phase of my existence in this wondrous mysterious world. From month to month, as I've said, all my powers have been declining. Never could I have conceived the immobility which aging has recently imposed on me. Yet now I must accept where nature has brought me and endure the weakening pulse of life. I've always had an element of religious feeling in my heart. Again and again, I've sensed, as I expressed it above, that in the universe—in the macrocosm and in the microcosm—there is a guiding power beyond our understanding. I sense that the life with which that power endowed all things—the vitality and awareness that we share with animals, the providential confluence of lives in love, the family, society, and the cosmos—shows a universal spirit, ever present but beyond expression in merely logical terms. I feel at peace, unafraid of becoming part of the unknown. I believe that our world in its entirety is sustained by a transcendent purpose pervading the nature of things of which I am a part.

R.H.C.
Carlisle, Pennsylvania
March 8, 2005

WORKS CITED

Fermi, Laura. (1954) *Atoms in the Family.* Chicago: University of Chicago Press.

Lala-Crist, Despina. (2001) *Nostos: Voyage of the Heart's Return.* Translated by Robert Crist. New York: Seaburn Publishing Group.

Lanza, Guy R. (2002) "Phytoremediations' Centenarian – An Interdisciplinary Journey Through Science." *International Journal of Phytoremediation,* 4: i-iii.

Libby, Leona Marshall. (1979) *The Uranium People.* New York: Crane Russak and Charles Scribner's Sons.

Lenhart, DeLance. (1978) *My Town: An autobiography of the author and an account of the town hegrew up with.* Atlanta: [privately published].

Rhodes, Richard. (1986) *The Making of the Atomic Bomb.* New York: Simon & Schuster.

Roberts, Royston M. (1989) *Serendipity: Accidental Discoveries in Science.* New York: John Wiley and Sons.

TIMELINE RAY H. CRIST

1900	b. March 8, Shepherdstown, Pennsylvania
1904-1911	Center Square Grammar School
1911-1916	Messiah Bible School and Missionary Training Home
1916-1920	Dickinson College, B.S.
1920-1921	Science Instructor, Williamsport-Dickinson Seminary
1921	Postgraduate Studies, Columbia University Assistant, Department of Chemistry
1925	Marriage to Dorothy Pauline Lenhart
1926	Columbia University, Ph.D.; Assistant Professor
1928-1929	Cutting Traveling Fellowship, Berlin
1929	Beginning of cooperation in research with Harold Urey
	Laboratory Manual developed
1937	Birth of son, Robert
1939	Establishment of Manhattan District Project, H. C. Urey, Scientific Director, Columbia Group
1940	Beginning of work with Manhattan District Project, Columbia Group
	Birth of sons, Henry and DeLanson
1945-1946	Scientific Director, Manhattan District Project, Columbia Group
1946-1959	Manager, Coal Hydrogenation Project, Director of Research and Development,
	Union Carbide Olefins Co., South Charleston, West Virginia
1959-1963	Director, Union Carbide Research Institute, Tarrytown, New York
1963-1970	Visiting Professor (Voluntary), History of Science, Dickinson College
1970-2004	Visiting Professor (Voluntary), Environmental Science, Messiah College
2004	At home on Devonshire Drive, Carlisle, Pennsylvania

Ray H. Crist

Awards and Recognitions

- Medallion, 1946. Columbia University World War II For Participation in the Division Of War Research.
- Honorary Doctor of Science Degree, *Dickinson College*, 1960
- Award for 25 Years of Modeling Excellence in Scientific Research, *Messiah College*, 1991
- Centenarian of the Year, *The Living Century*, 2000
- Distinguished Alumnus Award, *Messiah College*, October, 2000
- Lifetime Achievement Award, *Technology Council of Central Pennsylvania*, March, 2002
- Award as America's Outstanding Oldest Worker, *Experience Works*, May, 2002
- Certificate of Achievement, "Aging is About Living," *Pennsylvania Department of Aging*, October, 2002
- Award for Extraordinary Contribution in Voluntary Education, *Union Carbide*, 2003
- Lifetime Achievement Award, *Dickinson College*, June 7, 2003
- PBS feature series: *The Living Century—Ray Crist: A Teacher and Student for Life*, 2002
- CBS feature: Sunday Morning, narrated by Walter Cronkite, 2002.

PUBLICATIONS COLUMBIA UNIVERSITY

1. Morgan, J. L. R.; Lammert, O. M.; Crist R. H. 1924. Photochemical reactions in solutions of the alkali halides in acetophenone, *J. Am. Chem. Soc.* 46: 1170.

2. Morgan, J. L. R.; Crist, R. H. 1927. The photochemical decomposition of potassium persulfate. I., *J. Am. Chem. Soc.* 49: 16-23.

3. Morgan, J. L. R.; Crist, R. H. 1927. The photochemical pecomposition of potassium persulfate. II., *J. Am. Chem. Soc.* 49: 338-346.

4. Morgan, J. L. R.; Crist, R. H. 1927. The photochemical decomposition of potassium persulfate. III. The effect of added electrolytes, *J. Am. Chem. Soc.* 49: 960-966.

5. Crist, R. H. 1928. Ultra-violet transmission of a new window-glass substitute, *Ind. Eng. Chem.* 20: 1367.

6. Crist, R. H. 1930. The constricted mercury arc, *J. Am. Chem. Soc.* 52: 4337.

7. Crist, R. H. 1931. What are chain reactions?, *J. Chem. Ed.* 8: 504.

8. Crist, R. H. 1931. The construction and operation of capillary mercury arcs, *J. Optical Soc. Am.* 21: 690.

9. Crist, R.H. 1931. Reaction Charts, *J. Chem. Ed.* 8: 2251.

10. Crist, R. H. 1932. The quantum efficiency of the photochemical decomposition of potassium persulfate, *J. Am. Chem. Soc.* 54: 3939.

11. Smidth, L.; Crist, R.H. 1932. Method of plasticizing urea-formaldehyde condensation products, U.S. Patent 1,886,600.

12. Crist, R. H.; Murphy, G. M.; Urey, H. C. 1933. The isotopic analysis of water, *J. Am. Chem. Soc.*, 55: 5060.

13. Crist, R. H.; Dalin, G. A. 1933. Exchange reactions of protium and deuterium, *J. Chem. Phys.* 1: 677.

14. Crist, R. H.; Murphy, G. M.; Urey, H. C. 1934. The use of the interferometer in the isotopic analysis of water, *J. Chem. Phys.* 2: 112.

15. Crist, R. H.; Dalin, G.A. 1934. Exchange reactions of hydrogen and deuterium oxide, *J. Chem. Phys.* 2: 442.

16. Crist; R. H.; Dalin, G. A. 1934. "Isotopic equilibria" in the hydrogen-hydrogen oxide system, *J. Chem. Phys.* 2: 735.

17. Crist; R. H.; Roehling, O. C. 1935. The oxidation of carbon monoxide catalyzed by nitrogen dioxide, *J. Am. Chem. Soc.* 57: 2196.

18. Crist ; R. H.; Calhoun, G. M. 1936. The rate of oxidation of carbon monoxide in the presence of nitrogen dioxide, *J. Chem. Phys.* 4: 696.

19. Calhoun, G. M.; Crist, R. H. 1937. Reactions in the system containing nitrogen dioxide, carbon monoxide and oxygen; NO_3 as an intermediate in the classical trimolecular oxidation of nitric oxide, *J. Chem. Phys.* 5: 301.

20. Crist, R. H.; Wertz , J. E. 1939 Kinetics of the oxidation of hydrogen sensitized by nitrogen dioxide, *J. Chem. Phys.* 7: 719.

21. Crist, R. H.; Brown, F. B. 1939. Greaseless high-vacuum valve, *Ind. Eng. Chem., Anal. Ed.* 11: 396.

22. Brown, F. B.; Crist, R. H. 1941. Further studies on the oxidation of nitric oxide; the rate of the reaction between

carbon monoxide and nitrogen dioxide, *J. Chem. Phys.* 9: 840.

23. Crist, R. H. 1941. *A laboratory course in general chemistry*; New York: McGraw-Hill, 219 pp.

24. Weinstock, B.; Crist, R.H. 1948. The vapor pressure of uranium hexafluoride, *J. Chem. Phys.* 16:436.

25. Crist, R.H.; Kirshenbaum, I. 1957. Separation and concentration of isotopes of boron and oxygen, U.S. Patent 2,796,303.

RAY H. CRIST

PUBLICATIONS MESSIAH COLLEGE

1. Schreffler, Martha; Earlling, Michael; Crist, R. H.; Hoover, K. B. 1977. Uptake of copper ions by plant roots and algae, *Proc. Pa. Acad. Sci.* 51:163-5.

2. Frey, R. A.; Crist, R. H.; Oberholser, Karl. 1978. Copper-algae equilibriums in complexing solutions, *Proc. Pa. Acad. Sci.* 52: 179-82.

3. Sailer, D.; Shellenberger, D.; Crist, R. H.; Oberholser, K. M. 1980. Interactions of protons and metallic ions with algae, *Proc. Pa. Acad. Sci* 54:85-8.

4. Crist, Ray H.; Oberholser, Karl; Shank, Norman; Ming Nguyen. 1981. Nature of bonding between metallic ions and algal cell walls, *Environ. Sci. Technol.* 15:1212-17.

5. Crist, Ray H.; Oberholser, Karl; Shank, Norman; Nguyen Ming. 1982. Nature of the bonding between metallic ions and algal cell walls. Reply to comments, *Environ. Sci. Technol.* 16:441.

6. Weisbrod, Robert; Zercher, David; Hess, Gerald; Crist, Ray H. 1984. Interaction of metallic ions with red blood cells and stroma, *Proc. Pa. Acad. Sci.* 58:89-91.

7. Chamberlain, Marianne; Mann, Cheryl; Hess, Gerald D.; Crist, Ray H. 1984. Proton transport through red blood cell membranes, *Proc. Pa. Acad. Sci.* 58:233-5.

8. Crist, Ray H.; Oberholser, Karl; Schwartz, Dwight; Marzoff James; Ryder, Darryl; Crist, DeLanson R. 1988. Interactions of metals and protons with algae, *Environ. Sci. Technol.* 22:755-60.

9. Crist, Ray H.; Martin, J. Robert; Guptill, Paul W.; Eslinger, Jill M.; Crist, DeLanson R. 1990. Interaction of metals and protons with algae. 2. Ion exchange in

adsorption and metal displacement by protons, *Environ. Sci. Technol.* 24:337-42.

10. Crist, Ray H.; Oberholser, Karl; McGarrity, Jane; Crist, DeLanson R.; Johnson, Jill K.; Brittsan, J. Michael. 1992. Interaction of metals and protons with algae. 3. Marine algae, with emphasis on lead and aluminum, *Environ. Sci. Technol.* 26:496-502.

11. Crist, Ray H.; Oberholser, Karl; Wong, Barry; Crist, DeLanson R. 1992. Amine-algae interactions: cation-exchange and possible hydrogen bonding, *Environ. Sci. Technol.* 26:1523-6.

12. Crist, Ray H.; Martin, J. Robert; Crist, DeLanson R. 1991. Interaction of metals and protons with algae. Equilibrium constants and ionic mechanisms for heavy metal removal as sulfides and hydroxides, *Mineral Bioprocessing;* Smith, R. W.; Misra, M., Eds.; The Minerals, Metals, and Materials Society, Warrendale, PA; pp 275-287.

13. Crist, DeLanson R.; Crist, Ray H.; Martin, J. Robert; Watson, J. R. 1994. Ion exchange systems in proton-metal reactions with algal cell walls, *FEMS Microbiol. Rev.* 14:309-13.

14. Crist, Ray H.; Martin, J. Robert; Carr, Donald; Watson, J. R.; Clarke, Heather J. 1994. Interaction of metals and protons with algae. 4. Ion exchange vs adsorption models and a reassessment of Scatchard plots; ion-exchange rates and equilibria compared with calcium alginate, *Environ. Sci. Technol.* 28:1859-66.

15. Crist, Ray H.; Martin, J. Robert; Chonko, Joseph; Crist, DeLanson R. 1996. Uptake of Metals on Peat Moss: An Ion-Exchange Process, *Environ. Sci. Technol.* 30:2456-2461.

16. Crist, Ray H.; Hess, Gerald D.; Gagnon, Alan M.; Crist, Delanson R. 1996. Metal ion uptake and storage by brain membranes, *Proc. Pa. Acad. Sci.* 70:65-68.

17. Crist, DeLanson R.; Crist, Ray H.; Martin, J. Robert; Chonko, Joseph; Thuma, Henri. 1996. Ion exchange reactions in sorption of metals by peat moss, *Pollution Prevention for Process Engineers*; Richardson, P. E.; Scheiner, B. J.; Lanzetta, Jr., F., Eds; Engineering Foundation: New York; pp. 193-199.

18. Crist, DeLanson R.; Crist, Ray H.; Oberholser, Karl; Erikson, Jeffrey; Bennett, Jennifer; Noto, Louis. 1998. Ion exchange basis for biosorption and bioremediation of heavy metals, *Miner. Process. Extr. Metall. Rev.* 19:253-263.

19. Crist, Ray H.; Martin, J. Robert; Crist, DeLanson R. 1998. Nature of interaction of metal ions with acid sites of the biosorbents peat moss and *Vaucheria* and model substances alginic and humic acids, *Fundamentals of Adsorption 6*; Meunier, M., Ed.; Elsevier: New York; pp. 969-974.

20. Crist, Ray H.; Martin, J. Robert; Crist, DeLanson R. 1999. Interaction of metal ions with acid sites of biosorbents peat moss and *Vaucheria* and model substances alginic and humic acids, *Environ. Sci. Technol.* 33:2252-2256.

21. Crist, Ray H.; Martin, J. Robert; Crist, DeLanson R. 2002. Heavy metal uptake by lignin. Comparison of biotic ligand models with an ion exchange process, *Environ. Sci. Technol.* 36:1485-1490.

22. Crist, DeLanson R.; Crist, R. H.; Martin, J. Robert. 2002. A new process for toxic metal uptake by a kraft lignin, *J. Chem. Technol. Biotechnol.* 78: 199-202.

23. Crist, Ray H.; Erikson, Jeffrey; Tyson, Todd; Hollenbach, Nathan. 2003. Toxic metal ion exchange with extracted gills of rainbow trout, *J. Pa. Acad. Sci.*, 77: 94-100.

24. Crist, DeLanson R.; Crist, R. H.; Martin, J. Robert. 2003. Use of various forms of kraft lignin for toxic metal

uptake, *Adsorption Science and Technology*; Lee, Chang-Ha, Ed; World Scientific, River Edge, NJ; pp 413-416.

25. Crist, Ray H.; Martin, J. Robert; Crist, DeLanson R. 2004. Use of a novel formulation of kraft lignin for toxic metal removal from process waters, *Separation Science Technol.* 39: 1535-1545.

26. Crist, Ray H.; Martin, J. Robert; Crist, DeLanson R. 2004. Ion-exchange aspects of toxic metal uptake by Indian mustard, *Int. J. Phytoremediation* 6:85-94.

27. Crist, Ray H.; Rusenko, Bethann; Martin, J. Robert; Crist, DeLanson R. 2004. Toxic metal uptake by sunflower, switchgrass, and *Alyssum*, submitted for publication.

Ray H. Crist

Presentations At National Meetings And Conferences

1. National ACS Meeting, Atlanta, Georgia, 1990. (Presented by Karl Oberholser)

2. Engineering Foundation, Santa Barbara, California, 1991. (Presented by Robert Martin)

3. Federation of European Microbiological Society, Metz, France, 1994. (Presented by DeLanson Crist)

4. Engineering Foundation, Palm Coast, Florida, 1995. (Presented by DeLanson Crist)

5. Engineering Foundation, Big Sky, Montana, 1996. (Presented by DeLanson Crist)

6. International Adsorption Society, Giens, France, 1998. (Presented by DeLanson Crist)

7. Engineering Foundation, Stockholm, Sweden, 1999. (Presented by Jeffrey Erickson)

8. International Adsorption Society, Nagasaki, Japan, 2001. (Presented by DeLanson Crist)

9. United Engineering Foundation, Edinburgh, Scotland, 2002. (Presented by DeLanson Crist)

10. Third Pacific Basin Conference on Adsorption Science and Technology, Kyongju, Korea, 2003. (Presented by DeLanson Crist)

LIST OF ILLUSTRATIONS